KILL THY NEIGHBOR

Corrine Vanderwerff

One man's incredible story of loss
and deliverance in Rwanda.

Pacific Press Publishing Association
Boise, Idaho
Oshawa, Ontario, Canada

Edited by Kenneth R. Wade
Designed by Dennis Ferree
Typeset in 12/13 Adobe Garamond

Because of the sensitive nature of the circumstances surrounding this story, all names have been changed, and details of certain incidents have been either modified or presented in composite form.

Library of Congress Cataloging-in-Publication Data:

Vanderwerff, Corrine
    Kill Thy Neighbor : one man's incredible story of loss and deliverance in Rwanda / Corrine Vanderwerff
        p.   cm.
    ISBN 0-8163-1306-7 (paper : alk. paper)
    1. Genocide—Rwanda.   2. Rwanda—History—Civil War, 1994—Personal accounts.   I. Title.
    DT450.435.V36 1996
967.57104—dc20   95-43286
                                                                CIP

96 97 98 99 00 • 5 4 3 2 1

Contents

In memory of

those we cherished

"They shall be mine, says the Lord of hosts, my special possession on the day when I act. . . . For you who fear my name the sun of righteousness shall rise, with healing in its wings. You shall go forth leaping like calves from the stall."

Great is the Lord, and greatly to be praised, and his greatness is unsearchable.*

*Mal. 3:17, 4:2; Ps. 145:3, RSV.

Introduction

Like so many others, I reacted numbly when the Rwandan massacres exploded into the international media in April 1994, especially when reports began circulating about neighbors killing neighbors who had shared pews in the same church. "Christians killing Christians? How could such a thing happen?" My husband and I had lived and worked in that beautiful little country during the early eighties, and when our mission transferred us to Zaire, ties still linked us with many of the friendly, gentle Rwandan people. We worried about our friends and our former students. Were they still alive? Had any of them managed to escape? At the same time, we were not totally surprised by what was happening, although nothing had prepared us or anyone for the magnitude of the horror.

"My dear mother, how can I express our anguish?" wrote a former student who risked his own life to save friends, colleagues, and their families. Because of his bravery, several had escaped with their lives. "But," the letter continued, "we have seen thousands die from the blows of clubs and machetes. God could never be able to punish in such a manner. It could only be Satan himself who led the mobs."

KILL THY NEIGHBOR

At Mudende in the north, soldiers routed everyone from the women's dormitory on the Adventist university campus and demanded all Tutsis to identify themselves. "We can't lie," two of the girls whispered to their friends. They stepped forward. For their honesty, they were dispatched. On the spot. Before the horrified others.

At Mugonero Hospital, high on the mountains overlooking placid Lake Kivu, fleeing Tutsis crowded into the mission church. "Wait," begged the pastor when a frenzied mob arrived. "The children have asked me first to pray with them." He raised his hands toward heaven. Well-placed machete blows and grenades silenced him and all the others.

In another center, everyone—Hutu, Tutsi, young, old, rich and poor—was targeted. Only the fleet of foot escaped.

For several decades, Rwanda was considered as one of the most Christianized of the African countries. "How could something like this happen in a country with so many Christians?" Rwandan youngsters who grew up in the eighties, listening to reports of conflicts in other countries, thought, *That can never happen here.* Yet it did happen. Those who have been exposed to the Rwandan culture understand something of the complexity underlying the issues that pushed the mild-mannered Banyarwanda, as the people call themselves, into what has become known as the Tropical Holocaust. Thousands of innocent men, women, and children have perished. Probably every family in the country has been scarred by the massacres. Nevertheless, there are the good stories, the stories of escape because neighbor protected neighbor, because friend saved friend, and because Christians risked their lives for others.

In the central area, Hutu colleagues hid a Tutsi pastor in a pit and then covered it with their sorghum harvest, bringing him food and water during all the weeks until he could safely come out. In the south, Hutu neighbors hid a young Tutsi in their house by day and sent him by night into the high, leafy protection of an avocado tree. One night, he saw the mobs come and search for him, because his body was not among those already murdered, and they suspected he was there in that very house. His protectors gave no indication that they knew anything of his whereabouts. Later, like others who were hidden until safe passage could be bargained, he was smuggled away at night across Lake Kivu in a pirogue to Zaire's Idjwe Island.

From among the many stories of escape and miraculous protection, I've chosen to tell Richard's. His mixed Hutu-Tutsi parentage and mixed traditional religion/Christian upbringing sets his experience against a rich background—a culture where for centuries the premise of social inequality bound together an autocratic system of lords and vassals, where religion taught the need to appease jealous and spiteful ancestral spirits, where drunkenness traditionally marked prosperity, where the "shoulder must never be higher than the neck" and therefore the masses tend to do as the chief does, where educational achievement and business success have become passports to power, and where more than 60 percent of the population are classed as adherents to Christianity.

"How could such a bloody nightmare become reality in a country with so many Christians?" This question has been repeated by many. The maxim *we tend to become like the ones we worship and admire* is perhaps a major key in understanding how it could happen—the behavior of the role models and heroes we have does shape our own behavior. The kind of God we worship does determine the kind of persons we become. If our concept of God is jaded by cultural perceptions, then our behavior will be jaded by those same perceptions. Further, if we are divided in that worship, we are also divided within ourselves.

Kill Thy Neighbor does not pretend to offer definitive answers to the Rwanda problem, nor does it claim to provide a comprehensive cultural perspective. It does not intend to insinuate blame or lay accusations. It simply tells one man's story against the backdrop of his upbringing. If it helps you to recognize the need to look beyond the surface before categorically condemning anyone on either side of an ethnic conflict, then it has been worth the telling. If it has brought awareness that no country anywhere in the world is immune to human catastrophe, it has served a double purpose. If it has helped you to realize your own need to search out and know the truth about God, it has served the greatest purpose of all.

May you, with Richard, continue to search out the true God of the

KILL THY NEIGHBOR

Bible, Who asks nothing greater of His admirers than that we love Him with undivided hearts and that we love our neighbors as ourselves.

Corrine Vanderwerff
Lubumbashi, Zaire

"See You Soon"

"Another grenade attack." Richard dug his fingers into the ridges along the steering wheel and drew a deep breath. "Where's this going to take us?"

"Sha, Richard!" Cyusa's voice quickly levered Richard away from mulling over these latest news headlines. "What'd ya think of the last question on the biostatistics exam!"

"Huh-huh-huh!" Richard's throaty half-laugh brought him back into the close-knit lightheartedness. "That professor, now he . . ."

More talk of exams, classes, and the latest campus news filled the little Peugeot as it hurried along the highway, down into the valley and past the Rwasave Cooperative. None of the five in the car paid any particular attention to the long, sun-splashed rows of beans, tomatoes, onions, and other table crops in the gardens blurring past the windows. Nor did they give any thought to the fact that those very vegetables would soon be harvested and packaged and rushed onto a plane to be flown away and fed to the project's growing market in France. None of them even commented on the beautiful hues and eye-catching textures of the thickly treed Rwandan National Arboretum, which forested the upsweep beyond the gardens and rolled back toward the university's main campus. They had seen it all a thousand times before, had strolled the paths, had enjoyed the shade and parklike ambiance created by having so many different trees from so many different places in the world planted in one place. And it was so convenient to their residence halls. The forest and the gardens were simply there—a part of life as it was and should be, and they had no doubt that they would all see it a thousand times again.

"Sha, Aline!" Sylvie suddenly leaned forward as if she had just thought of something important, the Kinyarwanda *sha*, campus in-word for showing close friendship, tipping automatically from her tongue. "Which printer's doing your invitations?"

The sun created a quick pearling of miniature rainbows along Aline's hair when she turned, facing around just enough to speak over her shoulder. "I'm not sure; that's why I'm staying with my sister in Kigali this week. Invitations. Cake. Candles. Napkins. There's so much to do to get ready."

Richard held the old car to speed, and while the women deliberated about the best way to serve the cake at the reception, they raced through the valley, beyond the gardens, over a bridge, and up the next hill.

"Have you decided for sure on the date?" Lydia asked.

Just then, they rounded a curve. Richard wrenched the wheel to miss a cyclist who had been shunted wide onto the asphalt by the huge mound of green bananas lashed to his bike's carrier. Three chickens, legs trussed and beaks wide, dangled head-down from the top of the load.

"That, yes! August 28!" Aline seemed not to notice that they blasted at only a hair's breadth past the struggling cyclist and his chickens.

"Sha, Aline!" Richard cut in. "You haven't told me yet if you know how to make those fancy baskets, you know, the ones that every good woman . . ."

"Oh, Richard." She batted her hand toward him. "How many times do I have to tell you? You'll see. On our wedding day, you'll see."

He sneaked a quick glance sideways—her blue blouse, the clarity of her dark complexion, her high cheekbones, the upsweep of her hair—and he drew a deep breath, as if by inhaling he could better fix her image in his mind and therefore prevent it from fading during the week they would be away from each other. He often bragged about her, boasting to his buddies that she had the beautiful eyes of a young calf. She deserved nothing but the best, and that was one of the highest compliments a Rwandan man could give the woman he had chosen to be his wife. "I hope I'll like what I see," he teased.

"You'll see!" she repeated. "Just because I'm majoring in economics doesn't mean I've forgotten all our traditions. Our home will be . . ." She broke off suddenly and smiled. "You know that a groom mustn't know a thing about the gifts his bride will bring to the house on their wedding day. You'll just have to wait."

"Well, I'm profoundly glad I'm not my grandfather, who had to wait till his wedding day to see who his bride would be!" He clucked his tongue. "I like this modern way better, and I like what I see now."

"Oh, Richard!"

He chuckled, amused at the way she exaggerated the initial sound of his name, catching it with her tongue and turning it from a French *R* into the Kinyarwanda way of pronouncing it almost like saying *d* and *l* and *r* all at the same time.

"Richard's making final arrangements this week for the finishing work on our house, you know." She turned again to their friends sitting in the back. "We'll live there till he starts his residency. Then . . ."

He heard with satisfaction the trace of pride underlying her words, and the soft assurance in her voice as she spoke of their future together filled him with a momentary *all's-right-with-the-world* happiness that almost matched the panoramic beauty before them. Cotton-puff clouds flecking a rich blue. Banana plantings, green and verdant, covering the hillsides. Stately eucalyptus bordering both sides of the roadway. At the end of the next valley, distant hills crinkled together, chaining upward into the Nile-Congo Crest and northward toward the volcanic Virunga. Rwanda. The country of a thousand hills. The little Switzerland of Africa, some said, though Richard doubted that his country's conical, olive-clad mountains matched the rugged grandeur of the Swiss Alps. At least they didn't look like the Alps he had seen in pictures.

Overhead, the sun beamed down warm and steady, a rare treat during April, when rains are usually at their heaviest, making it a perfect day to begin what he hoped would be a good vacation. Though they had hardly more than a week away from campus, it would serve as a good breather before that last-quarter push, which would bring him to the final exams of medical school. This would also be his first real visit home in more than two years. He had been in close contact with his parents—that was matter of course with all the responsibilities they shared in preparing for the traditional engagement feast and the dowry ceremony. He had even visited with them in the home away from home they had set up when skirmishes between the rebels and the national army during the war of '90-'91 had nearly trapped them under their own roof. Since then, his father had also been overseeing the general construction of his house, but Richard hadn't driven out to where it was being built on the old home place since . . .

Abruptly he interrupted his own train of thought. "And tomorrow—in church—you'll say a prayer for us?"

"Oh, course!" Aline's reply came automatically. "I always pray for us. Besides, it's Easter."

"I know it's Easter. That's why we have the week off. Huh-huh-huh." The quickness of his deep chuckle and his mischievous grin served to steer the conversation back into a lighter vein. A mustache neatly accented his full features, and the impeccable way his shirt draped his huskiness gave him the air of a young man well-placed in this world. But it all was a cover for what he was really feeling inside. He didn't want the others to know about his uneasiness, especially not Aline. That morning, when the national news had reported more grenade attacks, he could not help but worry. Almost every day someone was killed. Three here. Two there. Another few elsewhere. In addition, two high-ranking politicians had been assassinated during the previous weeks. "Political killings," he repeated to himself now. "Maybe. But you don't have to be a genius to see that real underlying problem is all about ethnic." Since the beginning of the civil war, provoked when the Tutsi-dominated FPR (Rwandan Patriot Front) invaded the northern sector of the country from Uganda in

October of 1990, tensions between Rwanda's two main tribes, the Hutus and the Tutsis, had steadily worsened.

He glanced again at Aline, now chatting over her shoulder with their friends. She seemed so at ease, as if being beside him made her feel completely safe. That's how he wanted her to feel. As for himself, he felt he had known her forever, although she had walked into his life for the first time ever on a September afternoon in 1992, less than two years ago. He and Cyusa had been sitting with a group of fellows at the video, as they called the bench near the kiosk fronting the university entrance, when a group of young women strolled into view.

"New," Cyusa had remarked. "Must be coming to register."

The others began to analyze the prospective coeds, commenting on the new interest they would add to the campus, but Richard said as little as possible. He could hardly take his eyes off the one in the middle. Her bearing, the grace with which she walked, so much like his mother, yet . . . *I've got to find some way to meet that one,* he told himself. *I wonder who she is.*

With the faculty of medicine situated away from the main campus, he had no opportunity even to learn her name until the following month. Although the university had banned freshman initiation, second-year boys carried on a clandestine tradition called *umusoto*. During the first month of school, they randomly picked on the new girls, trying to catch one alone and badger her into expressing herself in a manner no Rwandan woman of good breeding would ever use. The young woman's responses would peg her on the boys' rating list. Richard began hanging around the younger fellows, hoping that one *umusoto* group or another might lead him to the woman he had seen, hoping, at the very least, to learn her name. One October evening, his plan worked. The next evening, he went to Aline's room.

"There's a gang coming to get you for *umusoto*," he warned. "If you'd like, I'll stay to protect you."

She had liked. The following October, they had become engaged.

So much like my mother, he thought again, remembering why he had been attracted to her in the first place. *So beautiful, so tender, so* . . . The word that came to his mind did not mean at all to him what it could have implied to others. "So Tutsi."

He was thinking of her manners, the way she carried herself, the quiet, gentle way in which she related to others, and not of her being a member of one tribe or another. Yet he could not escape the tribal implications. His own family had been torn apart because of inter-ethnic fighting when he was small, and he still felt the scars from all the years he had been without his mother.

Hutus say I'm Tutsi; Tutsis say I'm Hutu; both call me "Hutsi."

That new term was coming more and more into common usage, especially around the university. *And foreigners don't understand.*

Since all Rwandans speak a common tongue, Kinyarwanda, with French as their second national language and with the two main tribal groups, the Hutus and the Tutsis, sharing a common cultural heritage, it's easy for the casual onlooker to confuse the two peoples. Yet the differences between them are so great that when Richard was small, his mother had been chased away from their home because she was a Tutsi. No matter what democratic ideas and determinations had spread across the African continent during the early nineties, Rwanda still accepted no official blurring of tribal lines. In their patrilineal society, Richard, like his father, was Hutu. He and Shema and Marie-Pierre, his little sisters, though belonging to the group labeled in French as *hybrids*, were officially three little Hutus who belonged to their Hutu father and had been kept by him when their Tutsi mother was forced to leave.

Hutsi. He rolled the new word over in his mind. *Me. Aline . . .* That was one of the reasons why he had felt so drawn to her—she understood, she was part of the same ambivalence, she, too, was a Hutu who in looks and behavior strongly favored her Tutsi mother. That was only natural, for the behavior part, at least, because Rwandan mothers are responsible for educating their children in social graces and moral conduct. *All five of us here in the car Hutsi.*

His thoughts paused. Although Rwanda has no official middle group, most of their close friends were Hutsi. They could all comfortably associate with folks from both tribes, yet he keenly felt that the current buildup of political tensions was making it more and more difficult for them to be accepted by either side. He drew a deep breath, then spoke. "If the president and the others in Arusha this weekend manage to agree and to sign . . ." he began.

"Sha, Richard!" Aline's voice carried a note of playful warning. "You promised me not to talk of any of those terrible politics, especially not today. We have so many happy things to talk about. Right? Lydia? Sylvie? Cyusa?"

"Well, if he does," Richard continued as though he had not heard, "that may give us good reasons to be happy and to celebrate with our families this week."

"How about us getting together again at the Jacaranda?" Cyusa suggested. "Dinner one evening after vacation. On the balcony. Enjoy the view. And the company." Cyusa looked sideways at Sylvie. "I'm sure we can find plenty of reasons to celebrate, no matter how successful the president's talks are this weekend," he continued.

"Great idea!" Richard agreed. "How about the first Sunday after classes start again—to celebrate the good fortune of all of us?" For the university crowd, the Jacaranda was one of the favorite eating places in Butare. In fact, they had just come from having lunch there before starting the drive home. Then, almost before he realized it, they were whizzing along the straight stretch of highway through the last valley, past the lone tree where a colony of yellow-billed storks nested every year, and twisting up into the hills of the city. He dropped off the others, and then he was saying goodbye to Aline at her sister's place. She stood looking up at him, and he noted again the beautiful softness of her deep brown eyes. "It's going to be a long week without you." He sighed and drew her close. "Have a happy Easter!" he whispered.

She nodded, then murmured, "Good luck!"

He understood what she meant. A Rwandan man was expected to have a house built on the family lands before his marriage. It was not going to be easy to find a trustworthy carpenter with whom to leave all the finishing details and who would be certain to make it a home worthy of this gentle treasure he had found. "I'll need it." He smiled, kissed her lightly, and then turned toward the car. "See you soon," she called after him.

2

Inyenzi!

On Monday afternoon, when Richard walked into his father's bar with his boyhood chum Frank, men crowded around the tables as they always had, and the air mingled the tantalizing sweetness of roasting bananas with the gaminess of grilled goat's meat and the sharp headiness of beer and banana wine. A few platters with skewered brochettes and browned slabs of banana sat here and there among the dark-amber distillers' bottles. He recognized several faces—his second-grade classmate Haricot with a few of his buddies, the lot of them already under obvious influence; two primary-school teachers; three of his distant cousins who worked their families' holdings south of town; some former schoolmates; and several youngsters who, when he was a boy, would have been considered far too young to join the men at a bar. He followed Frank to an empty spot by one of the tables.

"What's the news from out there where you've come?"

Richard could not be positive about the face that turned toward him with that question after the general polite greetings had been spoken. Was it wearing genuine friendliness? Or was it merely a grinning mask waiting to hear words that could be taken and turned against him later? "The news is good," he replied, lapsing into the standard Kinyarwanda reply.

More easy talk followed; then someone asked, "And what news have you been able to bring us from our politician friends in Kigali?" Richard felt more than heard the quiet fall across the room and sensed that everyone had turned his direction to hear what he, the newcomer from the outside world, would have to say. "Will they be able to find any real solutions with which to solve our problems?"

Richard took a moment before he replied. As a university student, the son of one of the area's more prosperous businessmen and one who had also worked in the country's capital city of Kigali as well as having traveled to other parts of the country, even outside to Goma and Bukavu in Zaire, he was treated with a deference by the ordinary people in much the same way as they would show respect to a White. On the other hand, as a Hutsi of mixed Hutu-Tutsi parentage, he and anything he might say would be regarded with a certain suspicion in this predominantly Hutu crowd.

Since the war of October 1990, which had almost reached the borders of their commune, many Tutsi families had fled the community. At the same time, a flood of Hutus, displaced from their homes by the Tutsi-dominated FPR invasion, had crowded in to live with friends and family, filling all available room. The extras sheltered where they could.

When he spoke, his answer bore no likeness to the direct response of either an American or a European, assuming, rather, the roundabout logic of his ancestors, for he dared not appear to support any particular group, especially not the FPR. "It seems that if they can bring themselves to the point where they might be able to come to some semblance of agreement upon how to implement the terms upon which agreement has already been achieved, then we might be able to expect that they could bring themselves to the point where that agreement might be of some help toward reaching a solution to those problems that we have seemingly become prone to encounter."

Expressions showed that the men had taken his multitude of words very seriously. That is to say, the ones who had not yet reached a level of intoxication that would prevent them from following what was being said. "We'll see what news the president himself might be able to bring when he returns from Arusha on Wednesday," someone volunteered, but the conversation veered quickly away from politics to the more immediate and important matters of crops and cattle.

Richard followed the twists of the discussion, thinking of the four cows in the shed at his parents' place. Only four. All his father had now, hardly more than a token to replace those that had been stolen and slaughtered on the first day of the war three-and-a-half years earlier. After losing some animals to an epidemic of hoof-and-mouth disease in the eighties, they had rebuilt the herd to ninety-three cows, plus a number of young stock. Then by the nightfall of that unforgettable first day of October in 1990, all the animals were gone. Worse yet, one of their herders had been killed. Richard remembered the day as if it were only yesterday. He had gone up to spend the last of his school vacation at the ranch. As eldest son and heir, he was taken for granted as his father's representative in matters of management, and on the afternoon he arrived, Alphonse, a ranch neighbor, welcomed him.

"Come for a drink of milk," he invited.

Richard sat on the proffered stool while one of the women went to the milk cellar. Nearly ninety individual kraals filled the ranch in a villagelike layout. Every one of the ranchers would expect him to come, to sit, to drink. "As if my stomach is so big." He laughed within himself but aloud said a quiet *murakoze* (thank you) when the woman brought the wooden goblet. "It's good to be able to taste such fine fresh milk again," he complimented Alphonse. "At the university . . ."

One of the things he missed most was milk. At home it stood ready for the drinking at any and every time of day. No one ever thought of drinking mere water. Butter, too, was always there—for the table, for using as a skin pomade, for bartering. But then, his father was an affluent man of many cattle in this society where owning even one cow marks one as belonging to the bourgeoisie. A man would bind himself to work even ten years to have that cow. To refuse to drink its milk with him—unheard of! That simple act could create a lifelong enemy.

KILL THY NEIGHBOR

"Lions been ranging on our side of the park these last days, and the herders chased one last night." Alphonse motioned toward the southeast, where the ranch land bordered Akagera National Park, and in the back of his mind Richard remembered his aunt shouting, "Lions eat bad boys. And if you ever again . . ." He had been five then. "Then night 'fore last, another fellow lost three cows," Alphonse was saying. "Bandits. They been sneaking 'cross the river from Uganda almost every night these weeks."

The equatorial dusk came with its usual suddenness, and Richard stood to go. Wishing his friend to rest well, he walked into the filmy outer skirting flaring out from the dull bronze haze that hung toward the west. Full darkness, broken only by the glow rising up from fires already burning in a scattering of the enclosures, had settled during the scant minutes it took him to reach his father's place. With a quick twist, he levered out the stiff mat gating barring passage through the hedge, and he entered. *Home.* He thought more than spoke the word, taking a deep draw of the musky animal odor. Between the close-packed mass of heavy-boned animals and the dark hulk of their ranch house wavered the fire. It lighted the work area, and he could see one of the men leaning against a large cow, his hands working wads of grass along her spine and over her flanks. Another man squatted on the ground, head touching the broad side of the same untethered animal, one hand pulsing a white stream into the wooden jug he held in his other. A calf suckled at a nearby cow, set there to stimulate his mother's milk flow. The women joined them. After the polite and lengthy exchanges inquiring about the news of each one and his or her family, Richard went over to the cow and became part of the scene that was centuries away from the life he knew on campus. Absentmindedly he began scrubbing his fingers up and along her spine and between her long, splayed horns. "According to the news, the lions have been bad."

"Bad," that's what his aunt had said. "If you ever do that again!" And he remembered hauling back from her grip, trying to get away from the terrible sight of the beast stretched on the ground. It was huge. With long hair bristling around its head. The head had seemed taller than himself. Its mouth gaped open, and it had terrible teeth. "It caught a woman and ate her!" His aunt wrenched him forward.

"No!" he had shrieked. And had dug his feet against the slippery grass. "I won't! Never again!" He was afraid she would keep pushing him forward, toward the horrid animal that the hunters had deposited in front of the commune office.

"If you ever again . . ." Her words pounded on his eardrums.

"I won't! I won't!" he screeched. That morning, she had found his blanket and his mat wet, and then she had made him come with her to see the dead killer lion. "The lion will get you!" Her voice rose. "Bad!"

"Bad," the one milking repeated now.

"Huh-huh-huh." Richard chuckled to himself because he had never given his aunt a chance to make good her threat. Just then, one of the women came to take the full milk jug from the milker and leave him another. She slipped away, silent as a shadow, toward the cellar where she would empty it into a large, crook-necked storage gourd.

"The beasts have been many in these last times, and the herders from the far side chased one last night." The other herder spoke as though still talking to the cow to keep her standing quietly for the milking. "As Imana wills, we have not lost any animals. In any case, though, we are prepared." He held up his arm, and the firelight played along a dark something circling his wrist.

"Aieeee," agreed the milker. "And well protected." All the herders had great faith in the powers of the bracelets their divines prepared for them. "But should any animal dare to approach, it would never escape the medicine we have for our arrows and spears." Generally, the herders preferred to arm themselves in the same sure way of their ancestors—with bows and poison-tipped arrows and spears.

The women continued to slip quietly in and out, tending their share of the carefully divided farm responsibilities. Men herded and milked— a woman under no circumstance would milk a cow, any more than a man would presume to enter the kitchen hut to take over her cooking— while the women cleaned the kraal, carried away the manure in large baskets that they carefully balanced on their heads, lay clean bedding for the animals, and cared for the milk. Some of the milk they would make into butter, some they would send to the village for the family, and the rest would be sold to the creamery at Kagitumba. On the morrow, one or the other of them would carry the extra to that nearby border town where the Muvumba River joined the Kagera, forming the meeting point of three countries—Rwanda, Uganda, and Tanzania—before it flowed on its way eastward into the great Lake Victoria. The huge, dark shadows, wavering with the monotonous movement of the flames, continued their guard along the thickly matted pencil brush, creating the impression that the tall bushes formed a solid, impenetrable fortress. It was late when Richard finally went into the house and to his bed. That last week of September 1990 passed quickly.

"Some ranchers must know something we don't." Alphonse sounded puzzled that last evening of the month. "They've been taking herds across the river, grazing them on the Ugandan side."

"More grass for ours," Richard remarked offhandedly, though the wide, open rangelands on the northeastern savanna offered more than enough for all.

About midway into that night, he was startled awake by a loud, throaty roar. He pushed himself up onto an elbow. "Lion!" He started to swing his legs over the edge of his bed, then caught himself. "Naw. The herders are there." And he flopped down onto the mattress, rolled over, and went back to sleep. Toward dawn, he became aware of another sound. He rubbed his eyes sleepily, listening as a distant *rat-tat-tat-tat-tat* repeated itself.

"Shots?"

The sharp peppering echoed again and again.

"Bandits?"

He lay motionless, trying to read direction and meaning into the sound. "Must be a big group, all that noise." He waited, ears straining. The shooting continued. Finally, he slipped out of bed, pulled on his clothes, and went for Alphonse. "What do you think about this?"

"I don't know." Several volleys of rifle fire suddenly chained together toward their north like a half-dozen strings of super-large firecrackers that had been lighted at the same time. "Usually thieves sneak across the river; fire a few shots; take two, three animals; and leave. If those're bandits, they're certainly a very serious lot." Alphonse studied the sky beyond a distant bluff of trees as if looking for something that could explain the shooting. "Maybe we should hike to town and see if we can find some meaning for this."

By then, the sun had climbed well above the eastern forest, and insects had already begun humming on their unknown errands among clumps of the tan dry grasses. When the boys arrived in Kagitumba, a straggling of townsfolk milled along the streets. "An attack from Uganda!" The first one to respond with any authority to their questions, a bystander with grizzled face shaded under the sagging brim of his once-gray hat.

"Bandits?" asked Alphonse.

"No! Inyenzi!"

Inyenzi?

Just then, a huddle of peasants, subsistence cultivators with worn, disheveled clothing, dusty feet, and drawn faces, passed to their left. A man in the middle staggered, his shirt gapping back from a mangled shoulder.

"Inyenzi!" This time, the old man spat the word from between puckered lips, his ancient frame braced on wide-planted feet, his voice certain with the authority that came with his years.

"Inyenzi?" A dull chill slapped across Richard's back. Because of the Inyenzi, his grandfather had banished his mother, chasing her away from their family. He had been only a little fellow then, too young to remember, but he would never forget what his grandmother told him about them later. Tutsi guerilla fighters, they were, refugees who had fled the country during the independence wars, then started sneaking back and killing Hutus. They were cunning and fierce and would do anything to get back the power they had lost, she had warned. You never knew when they might attack.

The Hutus had been quick to fight back, and they had hunted down anyone they suspected of supporting the Tutsis. That's why his mother had to leave. Because of the Inyenzi fighters, like cockroaches who come in secret and hide, and no one knows they're there until someone opens a basket and finds that they've eaten holes in all the clothes. That's what the Hutus said the Tutsi fighters were—cockroaches. But the ethnic fighting had been capped in the late seventies, and to onlookers from the outside world, even to many Rwandans, the decade of the eighties appeared to have brought peace. And now in the first year of the decade of the nineties . . .

"Inyenzi?" Richard repeated, as if he could not believe what he was hearing.

The old man started to reply, but just then, two sets of four men passed them, carrying litters. And there was blood. Lots of it.

"The soldiers!" someone was shouting. "At the border. Dead! All of them!"

"I'd better go!" Alphonse swiveled around. "My family."

Richard nodded. Mute.

"Inyenzi!" the same voice was shouting. "Shooting everyone!"

"Run!"

Heavy footsteps pounded in from the other direction, many sets of them. Richard snapped his head around. Soldiers. From the local detachment. In full battle dress with guns and bullets and grenades. Some seemed to be taking positions along the street.

"What is this?" Richard called out to one.

"War!"

And in that word, Richard heard a fear that exceeded his own, the fear of a trainee who had never before been marched to real battle. The streets choked with people now. Townsfolk. Soldiers. Peasants. Some going this way. Some that. Some carrying wounded with mangled legs and gaping bullet wounds. Some pulling themselves along with walking sticks. Some, like he, simply standing and staring.

A loud roar rocketed overhead.

"The president's plane!" Shouts and cheers momentarily drowned further commentary.

"That's an army colonel on reconnaissance, not the president!"

"Of course!" Richard exclaimed in agreement with this new voice that spoke beside him when the pandemonium began to settle. "The president's in America at . . . Alexis!" he suddenly exclaimed, recognizing his friend from the creamery.

"Richard!"

"I was on my way to the creamery," Richard began. "But . . . what do you make of this?"

"Just like them!" Alexis shook his head. "Attacking while the president's gone." At the time, President Juvenal Habyarimana was in the United States attending a United Nations conference on the rights of children.

"Who's 'them'?"

"I don't know." Alexis turned, and Richard could see the worry lines in his friend's face. "But this must be real war!"

"Inyenzi murderers!" a woman screamed.

"Still. After thirty years without a king, these people behave with a mentality that needs a king. With the chief gone, they're like children without a mother." Alexis shook his head again.

"What should we do?"

"Do you have your driver's license?"

"Yes." Richard patted his pocket.

"We'd better leave. See that?" Alexis pointed along the side street toward one of the creamery vans. "Take it. I'll go get my car. That way we can save at least two vehicles."

Richard drove out first. He had barely reached the edge of town when a soldier stepped in front of him, gun in hand. "Documents?" he demanded.

Richard reached into the glove compartment and handed him the papers for the vehicle.

"Driver's license. Identity card."

Richard showed him the required pieces.

"This is not your vehicle."

"No," Richard started to explain. "I'm . . ."

"Get down!" the soldier ordered.

"But the creamery director is just behind me; he'll . . ."

"Down!" the soldier ordered again, this time motioning with his gun.

KILL THY NEIGHBOR

Richard opened the door and stepped out, expecting to stand by the vehicle and wait for his friend. In the same moment, the soldier waved to some comrades standing across the road. They ran over, jerked open doors, and clambered in. Richard jumped back as one of them gunned the motor. With grit spraying up behind its wheels, the van lunged back onto the macadam and ricocheted out of sight.

"Well, we tried," was all Alexis said when he found Richard stranded by the road.

Another military barricade barred their way at the edge of the forest. This time, the soldiers forced Alexis to hand over his car with all the belongings he had packed in it. Empty-handed, the two young men began trekking the thirty-six kilometers through the forest to the next commercial center, where they found lodging for the night. Throughout that night, armored vehicles roared in from Kigali with FAR (Rwandan Armed Forces) reinforcements. By the next morning, October 2, 1990, military surrounded the town—the national army on one side; the Inyenzi on the other.

3

"We're Here to Help!"

Conversation in the bar grew louder again, and a voice he did not recognize brought Richard back to the realities of life in April of 1994. "I assure you, after the president returns home on Wednesday from Arusha, the politicians will get down to being serious. Those FPR Inyenzi. Aach! Taking our houses and cows. Killers!" The man brought his fist down on the counter. "I'll tell you what ought to be done with them and their accomplices."

A displaced Hutu, his tongue loosed with too much banana wine. Richard accented his silent judgment by spearing another piece of grilled banana with the skewer of his brochette; at the same time, he wished all the ethnic politics would take themselves to another world. Across and to his left sat an old Tutsi neighbor, who neither by word nor expression showed that he understood the intention of what was being said. Even if the insults grew too explicit, Richard knew his old neighbor would not react. Not only was the old man a minority of one in the bar, but any Tutsi worthy of his mother's education knows how to master his feelings, masking them so that no one, then or later, will be able to read his true sentiments. Anything, though, that went beyond his personally accepted limits would never be forgotten, of that Richard was sure. Not ever. Not even if he had to wait a lifetime and then pass on his hidden grudges for later generations to avenge.

"Inyenzi!"

The word spat across the room again, this time arrowing from the embittered Hutu and toward the old man. "And simple death would be too kind."

The old Tutsi still gave no indication that he had heard.

Hate. Fear. Both, it seemed to Richard, had pushed the remark. Spearing another slab of banana, he, too, masked what he was thinking. Too many had lost too much during the war following the 1990 invasion, and with the push toward multiparty elections, he had already seen too much truth in what his father often said: "When someone's stomach is empty, give him something, and he'll go where you want and do what you want. For the sake of his own stomach, he'll keep his big brothers' stomachs full."

The Hutu banged his fist on the table now. "Death is too kind!" he snarled again.

Through the corner of his eye, Richard caught the raising of some bottles in silent assent. One was Haricot's. His insides knotted. Politicians definitely were using their young and hungry tribal brothers. That had become more and more obvious since the initial FPR attack on October 1, 1990. He would never forget that terrible day. Nor the events that followed. The next morning, Tuesday, after having fled the ranch and Kagitumba the day before and having spent a mostly sleepless night in a run-down hotel, he had decided to cut across country on foot and circle back to his parents' home. Alexis had found a ride to Kigali before daybreak, and Richard strode along the street, looking for a place where he could get something to eat.

"The army's over there—in the forest!" Three other displacees had joined him, and one gestured toward the east. "Preparing to attack!"

"And the Inyenzi pushed south during the night, just behind us," exclaimed another. "They're on the other side of town."

"Over there?" Richard pointed.

"And over there."

The two directions pointed out seemed to close in toward Richard like the jaws of a vice. If these men were right, the enemy blocked his way home. "Then which way are you going?" he asked.

"Kigali."

"Halt!" a sudden voice ordered from behind.

The other three stopped, and Richard tensed as if ready to crouch forward like a sprinter waiting for the starting gun.

"Everyone outside!" the same voice bawled, amplified by a megaphone.

Richard threw a quick glance over his shoulder. Several tall, lean soldiers dressed in battle fatigues marched toward them.

"Everyone out. Go to the central square."

Richard took a quick step forward. In that same instant, another group of armed soldiers rounded the corner ahead of him.

"We're good! We're your friends!" the megaphone soldier was shouting behind him. "You've suffered. We've come to liberate you." More soldiers marched into sight ahead of him, bayoneted rifles in their hands. "Everyone outside! To the central square! We're here to help."

Richard spun around now. Soldiers were everywhere, and people had started straggling from their houses to let themselves be scooped along as if being scooped forward by a large net. The one with the megaphone continued to shout. "We're your friends! We've come to liberate you!"

"Liberate? From what?" he wanted to shout. Seeing he had no choice, he let himself be scooped into the helpless mass and be shuttled with them toward the communal square. There they were stopped and forced to sit. More rifle-toting, fatigue-clad invaders ringed them. At last, the leader took the podium.

"You've suffered! We're here to help you!"

The message repeated itself in many words while the morning sun highlighted snags of dusty weed seeds and brown bits of dried grass and leaves against the knotted dark hair on many heads. The night had been unkind, and now there were the guards, lithe, alert, and heavily armed.

Well-trained. Richard tried to make sense of what he was seeing. *Maybe from the Rwandan and Burundian Tutsi refugees who helped put President Museveni in power in Uganda.* That had been four years earlier. A Hima, the Ugandan president, was from the same race as the Tutsis. The speaker's promises continued to blare from the megaphone.

"We've come to give you a better life. To liberate you from this dictatorial government."

Richard clapped and cheered with the others. He had grown up with rallies and leaders. They all had. They all knew that when a leader speaks in a single-party republic like Rwanda, everyone must applaud, especially when there are soldiers and guns.

"Prices are too high!" The megaphone voiced blustered on. "We'll fix that! How many of you would like better prices?"

"Yes! Yes! Yes!" Like robots, the crowd clapped and cheered some more. Like a robot, Richard echoed their supportive shouts.

"Then watch!"

A sudden staccato of shots ripped the morning, riddling the door of a shop across from the square. Soldiers rushed the building and kicked their way in. Moments later, they reappeared, shouldering cases of beer and boxes of packaged peanuts.

"Who wants beer? Two francs a bottle!"

Hands waved across the crowd.

"And peanuts!"

The looted goods quickly sold at these impossibly low prices.

"These will be our prices!" the spokesman promised. "How many of you want our new government?"

Again, Richard clapped and cheered with the others. Some, though, sat mute as though not understanding what was expected of them. Soldiers quickly singled them out, and, with their rifles, prodded them to their feet and marched them away. Shots echoed in the distance. Richard cringed. More and more shots followed until there was a steady barrage of gunfire.

"The FAR! The army!" Excited whispers leapt through the crowd. "Counterattack!"

Orders were barked.

The soldiers ran.

The people ran.

Richard ran too. Toward a path looping through the brush, away from the sounds of fighting and toward the highway to Kigali. As he rounded a bend after reaching the highway, he saw a barricade manned by heavily armed soldiers wearing the uniform of the national army. Smiling, he walked toward them.

"Who are you?" one demanded.

Richard gave his name.

"Your card!"

The look. The tone of voice. Richard's chest tightened. The Inyenzi were Tutsi and Tutsi sympathizers. There had been talk at the university about Tutsi revolutionaries inside the country who were collaborating with rebels who had fled. Rumors said they were stocking arms and awaiting the day that would favor an uprising. Suddenly, he was keenly aware of the features he had inherited from his own Tutsi mother—his pointed nose, his slenderness, his narrow feet. He held his card out to the soldier.

The soldier took it and studied it for a long instant, his finger tracing the line that said "Hutu." Then he looked at Richard, eyes narrowing as though to better examine the face before him. He said nothing.

Richard waited.

The soldier again looked down at the card, then, silently handing it back, signaled for Richard to proceed. At the next commercial center, he found a taxi. A few kilometers farther, they were stopped at another barricade.

"Everyone out!"

The order became routine. Barricade after barricade, they clambered out and stood to the side while the vehicle was searched—for guns, for ammunition, for grenades. Near Kigali, the taxi was stopped once again.

"Enemies!"

Every window of the vehicle framed a shouting soldier.

"Accomplices!"

33

KILL THY NEIGHBOR

Richard forced a calm exterior.

"Out!"

Climbing out had become routine. The passengers collected to the side.

"Put your vehicle there!" the post commander ordered the driver, pointing to the side of the road.

Richard looked a question at one of his fellows.

"Let's go!" the other hissed.

Everyone scattered.

CHAPTER 4

Prison

By the time he had reached the edge of Kigali and had wound his way through the back streets to his sister Annie's house, Richard had heard many stories as different as night and day.

"What's happening?" his brother-in-law Fredy asked. "Suddenly, the town's full of military, rumors say we're under attack, and last night they slapped down a curfew." In the background hovered Annie. Being the daughter of his father's older brother, she was considered, in the Rwandan way of counting family, as his elder sister.

Richard told what he had seen and some of what he had heard. Two days later, Kagabo, the neighborhood cell leader, banged on their door. "You're harboring an enemy!" Kagabo fixed cold eyes on Fredy. "We've seen the one who came before yesterday."

"The only one who is here is my wife's little brother, who fled when the enemy invaded Monday morning," Fredy responded. "If you want, I'll call him so you can talk to him."

"I'm calling the military!" Kagabo blustered. "How do we know you don't have a stock of guns hidden in your house?"

"There are no guns to be found here." Fredy's voice remained even.

"The city's on alert," he explained to the others after Kagabo was gone. "I heard on the news this morning that all cell leaders have to report any strangers who've arrived in the area of their jurisdiction. He's only doing the duty for which we've elected him."

Years earlier, the government of President Juvenal Habyarimana had divided the entire country into administrative blocks somewhat following the pattern of the old Mwami feudal system, which had been adapted by the Belgian administration. Now the smallest unit, the cell, was made up of about thirty families, with the number varying according to the population of the area. A group of cells made a commune, a group of communes made a sector, and a group of sectors made a prefecture. The country itself was divided into ten prefectures, with a few of the larger ones being divided into subprefectures. Each cell of families elected a committee of five representatives, with the one receiving the most votes becoming cell leader. In effect, politically, he took the place of the little hill chiefs who had traditionally headed extended families. Thus Kagabo had become their cell leader. What Fredy had not bothered to explain to the others after the visit was Cell Leader Kagabo's aggressive behavior.

Richard looked around at the family, and he began to understand something that he, also, did not want to talk about. Fredy and Annie, as well as he himself, had Tutsi mothers. Even though they were legally Hutus, full-blooded Hutus did not trust the half of their heritage that was Tutsi.

At the high heat of noon the next day, they all sat in the shade on the veranda. Sudden footsteps thumped into the yard, giving the impression that someone had jumped over the wall, then run for cover. Richard swiveled around. Just then, he saw two soldiers clear the wall and, after landing with a double thump, dash behind the mats screening the garden. A bayoneted rifle already protruded through a bush. The gate burst open. More soldiers rushed in. Fredy, Annie, and Richard stared. The children sat like little brown statues. No one dared say a word. An entire platoon, it seemed, dashed in and surrounded the house while a squad, rifles leveled, advanced toward them.

"Where are the enemies?" demanded one.

Behind the soldiers stomped Kagabo. "That one!" The cell leader's arm jabbed in Richard's direction.

Instinctively, Richard ducked. In the same instant, someone grabbed him by the nape of the neck and jerked him to his feet. A cold, round, metal something shoved against his skin.

A gun!

"Where are your arms?" Bands of bullets crisscrossed the battle fatigues of the soldiers who vaulted onto the veranda and circled the little family.

"We have no guns or weapons," Fredy replied, and Richard was proud of the calmness in his brother-in-law's voice. "But you're welcome to look if you wish, and all that you are looking for, you can have if you find it."

"Show us." With his gun, the squad leader motioned Fredy to his feet and toward the door into the house.

The unseen gun in the unseen soldier's hand still pressed steadily against the back of Richard's neck. He stood rigid, hardly daring to breathe. The sounds of many footsteps echoed through the house. At one point, Fredy passed him, carrying a ladder and talking to someone about the trapdoor into the attic. At last, the soldiers began to regroup, this time more casually. Suddenly, the gun jabbed harder against Richard's neck. Instinctively, he stepped forward. The gun continued to propel him, through the gate and down the street, to join more men and women standing silent and unmoving before more guns. A dump truck came. They were muscled aboard, then dropped at the city's Nyamirambo stadium to join the multitude on the soccer field, already hunched in silent groups under glowering military guards.

"*Igicucu!*" Insult followed Kinyarwanda insult. "*Igicucu!* You foolish shadows! You don't care about our country! Fools! You don't care about our republic! All you want is to bring back your Tutsi king. All you care about is to work with your *FPR* friends and make us slaves to your old monarchy. *Inyenzi!*"

The last word Richard understood, and fear tightened around him like a straitjacket. He had run from the invaders, the Inyenzi, and now he crouched, immobile on the grass, one of five thousand accused of collaborating with those same Inyenzi.

More insults and more harangues about something called the FPR followed. "The Rwandan Patriotic Front!" The soldier shouting stamped his foot down and spun around, his gun now pointing toward Richard. "Patriots?" He made a gruesome face and spit toward those nearest him. "Traitors! All of you!"

That day. That night. The next day. No one dared speak. No one dared move, not even to answer the call of nature. Children cried. Parents couldn't reach out to console them. A pregnant woman in the next group aborted. No one was allowed to go to her aid. If anyone had the mischance to forget the surroundings and to speak, to even make a gesture toward someone else, soldiers soon came, guns trained, and motioned that one to join one of the silent groups who were selected at random and marched away, never to be seen again. Others, too, were taken, for who knew what reasons. Richard huddled in his allotted space with only one question burning in his mind.

Will I be next?

About noon the next day, huge caldrons of sorghum gruel were rolled in. Soldiers carried portions from group to group. But who had a plate? Or a cup? Or a utensil of any kind? Some clasped their hands together and held them out for the watery substance, which quickly seeped away between their fingers. Others lined their hands with a piece of their clothing, only to have the liquid sieve through. Others, though, were more successful. Copying them when his turn came, Richard held his shoe up, and a soldier ladled it full.

Another day passed. Then, on the next day, they were called by lists, according to home sector, marched away in groups, and loaded into vehicles.

"Prison."

The one-word sentence was pronounced in an incontrovertible manner, and that night his group was herded into the stadium of their home sector, moved from the Kigali stadium, it was rumored, because of pressures from the international community. The following day, the burgo-master, with local military personnel, came to transport them to the prison.

"Richard!" The burgomaster, who had known him from school, did not try to hide his surprise. "Why you? Never mind. Wait here. I'll take you home when I'm finished." And so it was that Richard became one among the few fortunate who were spotted by an influential friend and released.

After a few weeks, the FPR invasion was repelled by the national army. A second and stronger invasion brought the country to the Arusha Accord, which gave in to the Tutsi-dominated FPR's insistence that they have a share in multiparty rule. Idealistic talk about democracy and multiparty elections resulted in the formation of eighteen parties with varying political platforms. Before long, almost every party showed signs of splitting into two factions—one pro-presidential, the other pro-FPR. No matter how anyone tried to explain away this phenomenon, it was soon obvious that the factions had polarized along ethnic lines, and the concept of democracy as it was being played out did not allow for anyone to assume a moderate, mediating role.

And now, in his father's bar that warm evening of April 1994, Richard could see that the hard-line ethnic divisions were still as solid as ever.

CHAPTER 5

The President

Richard rolled over, yawned, then fumbled for the edge of his blanket. He started to pull it over his head to blot out the morning sun, which already glared across the window—vacation gave him the luxury of not having to get up until he wanted. He yawned again. Then, out of habit, started to reach toward Frank's old radio. With all his younger brothers and sisters also at home for Easter vacation, he had chosen to stay with Frank, and on their way back from the bar the evening before, they had tried again to find the contractor his father had recommended. And again they had failed.

"If I can't find that fellow today . . ."

Richard stifled another yawn. In a way he envied Frank. No Rwandan family of any standing would consider giving their daughter in marriage to a man who had not yet constructed a house, and Frank had his, ready and waiting. On the other hand, Richard felt sorry for his friend. The woman Frank loved had been given by her family to another man, one better able to satisfy their demands for more dowry cows than his teacher's salary could provide. *He'll easily find someone else*, Richard thought offhandedly. *He's a good sort, dependable.* For the moment, though, he was more concerned with his own problem.

Maybe I'll have to settle for some other contractor.

It was Thursday. Already. In order to pick up Aline and the others and then drive back to the campus in Butare in time, he needed to be in Kigali by noon on Sunday. With their wedding following so closely after final exams, he wanted to complete all the arrangements for the house no later than the next day. He flicked the radio's switch—he always listened to the news first thing every day when he woke up—and tuned to the national network. Somber notes diffused through the scratched, silver-colored grating on the large speakers of Frank's old radio and expanded toward every corner of the sleeping room. "Classical music!" He stiffened and flung back his arm. "Not again!"

"You said . . . ?" Frank roused and pushed himself up on his elbow. Then he, too, stared in the direction of the radio. The bleak strains continued. "Who now?"

Classical music on national radio. This early in the morning. That could mean only one thing. Minutes stretched impossibly long before the refrain faded and they finally heard the newscaster begin careful reading of a prepared bulletin. "The minister of national defense regrets to inform the population of Rwanda that the airplane bringing the presidents of the Republics of Rwanda and of Burundi . . ."

"The president! Our president?" In a daze Richard took in the details.

"Last evening when returning from talks in Dar es Salaam in Tanzania," the voice explained, "the plane was attacked—by enemies not yet identified—and shot down. None of the fourteen persons aboard survived the incident." Slowly and carefully, the list of all fourteen names was read. The first name cited was that of Rwandan president Juvenal Habyarimana.

"Dead."

The idea did not want to fit into logical sense.

"His plane shot down."

Momentarily, Richard's mind replayed a snatch from a not-many-weeks-earlier afternoon. "Sha, Richard!" the Intore troop leader had called out to catch his attention. "We need you for this one." When he had been younger and slimmer, he had danced regularly, and now as a backup dancer and in spite of the weight he had gained, the hard-paced athletics of the traditional Intore dances still came easily. Through the centuries, the Intores, the elite youth corps, had entertained at the Mwami's royal court with their disciplined, closely choreographed storytelling dances. Every school, every commune still had its Intore dancers.

Suddenly, he heard the drum choir slip into a new rhythm. He poised. Then he was bounding out onto the field with the others, feet slapping the earth, the bells around his ankles clacking in time with the others in his line and blending into the multipart rhythms of the dance. He leapt and twirled, the long, white raffia hair tied around his head flowing and bobbing, his wooden spear sweeping up and out in graceful moves. At times, poetic voices chanted above the rhythms; at times, the dancers' calls dominated; at times, a cow-horn solo triumphed. At other times, they simply danced, hard and fast, and he could feel the sweat building along the straps crisscrossing his naked chest as the group paid this beautiful tribute to the presidential airplane. Since the French government had accorded the plane for the use of President Habyarimana, dance groups around the country honored it with at least one and often several of the folkloric pieces at the public festivals where they performed.

"Richard."

The festive scenes faded, and he was hearing Frank's voice in the distance. And then he was hearing the announcement repeat itself.

"The minister of defense further requests that all citizens remain calm," the newscaster's dull tones continued, "and that they stay at their homes and that they not give in to discouragement because of this sad news."

Heavy classical strains again pushed through the old speaker to fill the void of silence that had fallen. Neither of the young men spoke for several minutes. "The president," Frank finally said, as though he did not believe the words he was repeating.

"The president," Richard echoed. And then neither said anything further. When at last Richard found the courage to get up and go to the window and look out, the streets were deserted. It was as though the entire community of people had disappeared. No voices filled the

morning. No one carried sweet potatoes or tomatoes or corn or peanuts or any of the usual goods toward the market. No children passed
with jugs for collecting drinking water. Nor did the usual assortment
of small boys jostle one another for possession of the dried banana
leaves rolled and twined into a serviceable sphere for their nearly nonstop matches of street soccer. The morning was empty. Morbid. As if
everyone had been swallowed into some sinister abyss.

"Things will not go well," Frank said at last.

"I think . . ." Richard turned and faced his friend. He was thinking
of Aline. In Kigali with her sister. "The army must be on total alert."

With six hundred FPR soldiers stationed in the capital since the
Arusha Accord, and with at least two highly placed Hutu leaders already having been assassinated in the preceding three weeks, the national army would, of course, be on battle alert. Suddenly, Richard's
tongue loosened and, alone in the presence of his closest and most
trustworthy boyhood friend, he allowed himself to express thoughts
that he dared confide only to him.

"The military have to know who those enemies are who have not
been named, the ones who have gunned down the president's plane,
and no citizen with any intelligence will refuse to cite the FPR as
being the ones responsible. The Inkotanyi! Who else?" *Inkotanyi*, an
old word dating back to an elite troop of warriors who served the
ancient Mwami, frequently replaced *Inyenzi* as term of reference to
the Tutsi forces. "Now. Two Hutu presidents of two Hutu-Tutsi countries. Dead. And too many Hutus killed during Tutsi raids since 1990.
Too many Hutus displaced by the war. Too many."

The two looked at each other. When it came to matters of revenge, Hutus and Tutsis stood at opposite poles. While Tutsis mask
their feelings and bide their time, Hutus are openly explosive. On the
other hand, Hutus are more willing to forget old grudges and accept
reconciliation, while the silent Tutsi pride will never leave unanswered
an old injury, even if it means waiting generations.

"Aaaaahhhh, Frank." Richard heard himself saying words he did not
want to pronounce. "There'll be blood." Gruesome details of earlier wars,

recounted by his father and his grandfather, filled his thoughts. Hutu brutality, once unleashed, was unimaginable. Yet the Tutsis would be sure to employ all their cunning, even at great human cost, in an effort to manipulate the end score against their Hutu enemies. "And it won't be only military against military," he predicted. "The president!" Again he shook his head. "Hutu extremists will have revenge. Quick revenge." He shifted nervously, braced his elbows on the window ledge, and stared into the distance as if studying some omen. "Whatever happens, the Tutsi purists will never stop this time. They will never be satisfied until they have back the power of rulership that they believe is theirs alone by gift from Imana. If Imana wills." Richard paused. "What is the will of the all-powerful Imana?" he wondered.

"What are you going to do? What should we do?"

Richard looked blankly at his friend, suddenly too aware of the complex antecedents that would be fighting to determine their immediate future. Many Tutsis of the ruling class had fled to surrounding countries during the wars of independence. They looked down on their tribal brothers who had stayed behind in peace with their Hutu neighbors and the Hutu government. The president belonged to the Hutus of the north. The northerners had always fiercely resisted domination by the ancient Tutsis. Those same northerners didn't trust the southern and eastern Hutus, who intermingled and even intermarried with the Tutsis. The 1990 FPR invasion had from the outset pitted tribe against tribe. Yet in the complicated intertwining of ethnic intrigue and regional mistrust, the conflict splintered into subconflicts. Hate flared into the open—some of it stemmed from colonial times and independence struggles; some reached back into the dim history of their peoples. Fueled by personal aspirations and jealousies and interfamily conflicts, it blackened attitudes on all sides.

"What can we do?" Richard half turned, the morning light outlining his husky profile, and he slowly shook his head. "Whatever happens, I predict that the FPR will find some way of making the world think the Hutus are alone responsible." He paused, abruptly, and then his natural positive outlook pushed to the fore. "Sha, Frank, my friend. The moderates of both sides will of course be masters of the situation and hold their own in check." He forced a smile. "We're lucky, you know. Being able to talk to and understand both sides. Then, when everything's settled. . . ." Suddenly, he interrupted himself. "But if you had to make a choice, to choose one side of your family or the other, whose side would you take?"

He continued to lean against the rough-hewn window ledge and now silently regarded the rutted street that passed a series of houses before it looped around the old tribunal building with its pocked, one-time cream-painted walls and the former commune offices and then turned and disappeared. From memory, he traced the way it wound down and through his grandfather's old fields. On one side, behind a wide stretch of bananas, was the tall hedge encircling his grandfather's old home place with its inner dividing hedge between the house of his father and Olive and that of his grandparents, which now stocked the family's sorghum harvest. On the other side, sheltered by the eucalyptus trees bordering the old calf field, stood his own nearly completed house. The main road cut across the slope above, leading through the center, past the market and between an assortment of commercial buildings: the tall, square maize depot with its pealing aqua paint; the flat cream-and-pink general merchandise store with its high cement veranda; a handful of other businesses and more houses. On the rise behind the market and adjacent to the bar, like a master overlooking its domain, was the house of his father and his mother. Softly he rephrased his question.

"Who would it be—my father or my mother?"

CHAPTER

6

Why This?

At ten that morning, the streets were no longer empty. Living so far from the capital and having no police to enforce the curfew, the country folk naturally gave in to their inherently curious natures.

"Did you hear the news?"

"How do you see things?"

"Where do you think this will take us?"

Apprehensively, they searched for someone, anyone, to give them answers regarding their immediate future. But under the façade of all their other questions lurked the dominating but unspoken worry: "Who killed the president?"

"Inkotanyi!"

A withered little Hutu spat out the word. Her ancient red plaid cloth, knotted in traditional style over her right shoulder, billowed out from her tired wraparound skirts like a dilapidated, off-colored tortoise's shell as she leaned against her walking stick. Her watery eyes peered up at Richard. "We're all going to die!"

"Grandmother, you should not let yourself think like that."

From the stoop, Richard observed her and the haggard mien of those clustered with her, coming to those better placed than themselves who could give them answers to this terrible thing that had happened. An old man, a castoff suit jacket bagging over the once-white cloth that draped from his waist, barefooted, spread his leathery toes as if to hold his sagging frame in better balance. A young woman, hair knotted and dusty, bounced a runny-nosed child on her hip. A young man, perhaps her husband, tan shirt torn at the shoulder, trousers bagging, stood mutely behind her. And there were the others for whom life had become equally arduous. And children. Ragged, in groups of a dozen or twenty, standing, looking, eyes wide but seeing nothing that would tell them what the future might hold for the next day, or even for that same afternoon.

"Do not say such a thing, for Imana does not will that we should loose hope."

"Then what do you think?"

More passersby had collected, their feet mushing the rain-softened earth, treading the section that scooped a hollow between Frank's house and the street into a miniature marsh. Three neglected clumps of stubborn, knee-high grass, clinging to basket-sized clods, struggled to maintain a hopeful touch of green. Although a little black listening box of some form, either somewhat new or very old, sat in nearly every peasant home to capture reports from the national radio service, nothing specific had been communicated to the population that day. Nothing, that is, other than the stark announcement of the plane's downing and the president's death, along with the order that all remain in their homes until further notice. Now they waited for Richard to translate to them what he had heard as he switched from one shortwave band to another on the little transistor he carried, listening as the world, for the first time in his memory, gave nonstop headlining to their little country. He turned from RFI (Radio France International) to the BBC (British Broadcasting Corporation) and on to the VOA (Voice of America).

"It seems the FPR have again taken up their arms and are marching on Kigali."

Inkotanyi!

Like a contemptuous epithet, the ancient title buzzed through the crowd. Many had lost homes, family members, and herds to the invaders, the FPR.

"Advancing?"

"Murderers!"

Richard consciously resisted the inclination to separate himself from the mounting anger and take cloister with his radio in one of Frank's back rooms.

The next day, Hutu peasants arrived with news of their own, collected, it seemed, from information that was being hopped from community to community as though sped on the wings of locusts. Killings. Of Tutsi collaborators. In the north, the president's home region. By militia squads and loyal supporters of the president—the Interahamwe. The reports were repeated with too much satisfaction for Richard's ease of mind. Only a few months earlier, *Interahamwe* had referred only to the harmless youth movement of the MRND, the president's party. "They found more than two hundred Inkotanyi accomplices on the Adventist University campus in Mudende. Hiding. But they took care of them, they did."

The claim, voiced by a toothless old man to the accompaniment of much head nodding, agreed in part with the international news accounts Richard was hearing—at least about the killings. But instead of talking about Inkotanyi traitors, the RFI, BBC, and VOA reported brutal scenes of innocent men, women, and children being slaughtered by militia and Hutu villagers who had chased after them and onto the campus—because they were Tutsi. University staff had tried to bargain with the pursuers, had tried to stop them. But had failed. "It's bad!" When Richard spoke under his breath in French to Frank, he meant not only the massacre in Mudende and in other northern areas named on the news, but also the attitude of the crowd gathered in front of the house.

Conflicting reports came from Kigali. "The FPR have attacked! Hutus are fleeing, and the government has gone south to Gitarama," said some. "No. The government troops have launched an offensive. They're pushing back the rebels," claimed others. "Interahamwe are *cleaning* out the accomplices." Richard winced at the triumphant tone curling around the word *cleaning.* By evening, he and Frank could see smoke rising above sections of forest to their north and west. "By local Interahamwe," bragged a neighbor.

With their area fringing the original war zone and lying not far south of the section ceded to FPR control by the Arusha Accord, as well as being crowded by displaced Hutus, the predominant sentiment was fiercely anti-FPR. All these factors added to making them vulnerable to attacks by terrorist factions from either side. The next morning, they saw people passing, haggard, clothes torn and filthy, carrying bundles and rolled mats, cooking kettles and clay pots.

"They're burning houses. Killing cattle. There." And whether Tutsi, Hutu, or Hutsi, they all pointed over their shoulders into the distance from which they had come.

"What do you think we should do?"

Neither Frank nor Richard could offer a good answer to the question they asked each other that evening.

"Why this?" They continued to toss questions back and forth, far into the night. "Why are our leaders so blind? Why can't people see that this is not the way? That this will only lead our country to ruin?"

"Because of our heritage," Richard had insisted. "All the centuries that the Hutus were dominated by the Tutsis. Then both had been under the colonists. Then since the Hutus took control of the government at independence, the Tutsis have been looking for a way to get back into power." He quickly abridged facts they both knew. "Besides, neither side trusts the other. Hutus think all Tutsis are dishonest. Tutsis consider Hutus as nothing but brutal. And for us Hutsis, we . . ."

"But the people today," Frank interrupted. "Running. Like hunted animals—in our country, the country that is known for being the most Christian in Africa?"

"Maybe it's the will of Imana." The idea flashed automatically into Richard's mind. He had grown up hearing that phrase—the will of Imana, the will of that distant supreme god of their ancestors.

"Maybe it's the will of the gods we've created for ourselves." Frank paused and looked toward the opposite wall. Richard followed his friend's gaze, and his eyes fixed on a wooden cross, a crucifix, its simple brown standing out against the wall's dull blue paint. "You know, Richard." Frank lowered his tone now. "After teaching for these years and watching how our children grow, I've come to the conclusion that people are like their gods. Even more, I have the impression that men create for themselves the kind of gods they want to worship. Oh, most of my students say they come from Catholic families, but you know as well as I do that many of our people really haven't forgotten our ancestors. No one could invent a god that is meek and gentle like Jesus, but we can easily make ourselves believe in gods and spirits who are jealous and treacherous like ourselves. I wish I knew more people like the Bible Jesus. But just look around. Visit the homes of our neighbors. No matter how Catholic or how Protestant they claim to be, you'll see signs showing that too many still observe rites intended to ward off the evil of the ancestral spirits."

As Frank talked, Richard's mind carried him back to an evening, one of many when the family elders had gathered with his grandfather in their round, mud-daubed stockroom. He had crept in after them, squatting in the shadows by the wall while they gathered with their calabashes around the fire, nursing the heavily alcoholic banana beer through their long, stiff reed straws. The flames danced up from a mound of dry branches in the center of the room, and a thin thread of smoke spiraled upward, adding another layer of soot to the already-blackened overhead thatch. At random, the men tossed dry sorghum into the flames.

"Hear that?" His grandfather pointed when another series of the tiny kernels popped and flares of sparks shot out. "The spirits are happy. The fire is burning away evil." He took a long draw on his drinking straw, then, turning, blew a spattering of droplets onto the earthen floor. "For the spirits," he said, and the others copied him, blowing drops of beer all around their circle. "So that even in the other world, they can continue to have the happiness of drinking with us." The old man blew another scattering of drops onto the floor, and in the firelight Richard saw that they quickly disappeared. "We must be careful not to offend them. We must keep them happy, otherwise . . ."

"You know all this yourself," Frank was saying.

Richard nodded and then, as if to counter his friend's theory, said, "But at the university with all the learning of science and philosophy we find that people are the builders of their society; and that in the evolutionary scheme of nature, people must be the ones to use the tools that they have and with them create a social ambiance that will change the world for the better."

Now morning had come once again, and Richard, unable to find escape in any further sleep, had placed himself at Frank's window, which framed the undulating savanna. Peaceful and calm like the friendly exteriors of both groups of his people, it rolled toward the dawn. Gone were the distant staccatos of automatic weapons that had disturbed their night, and gone, also, were the whooping calls signaling for anyone who had ears to come and help. He looked out into the expectant silence, waiting, as it always did, at the edge of any new day. Banana fields lifted thousands of arms upward in broad-leafed anticipation. Corn. Sorghum. Sweet potatoes. Beans. Beyond the bananas, scores of gardens and family fields spread the rolling lands with their life-giving substances, and in the distance, the out-of-synch morning duet of a pair of ibises announced to all and sundry that it was time to be up, to recommence life and be about the normal duties of another normal day.

He also heard subtle cow sounds. Well-placed families corralled cattle within their home parcels. At his father's house, Malachai would soon be carrying a ration of banana leaves and salt to their cows and scratching their hides and speaking soothing words as he began the day's milking. The four new cows in no way compensated for the large herd lost to the FPR, but knowing they were there gave Richard an assurance and in some strange way added to his hope that the situation would soon calm. Malachai, too, added a sense of security. Almost since he could remember, Malachai had been there like a steady older brother, seeing to their fields and guarding and caring for their cows.

Life and cows belonged together. They always had since the hidden centuries when his Tutsi forebears brought their cows and settled between the two large lakes of the central grasslands, Lake Muhazi and Lake Mugesera, where his Hutu forefathers already cultivated the rich land. Gradually the two cultures assimilated into one in which cattle played the leading role. Although no written history predates the arrival of the Europeans to tell exactly how this had happened, traditions and the oral records of the chroniclers of the Mwami's royal court give all, both Hutu and Tutsi, a rich understanding of their heritage. Before either had arrived, though, the Twa, the third ethnic group of Rwanda, were there. Nomads, they preferred to keep themselves aloof from the others, roaming the forests, hunting buffalo and other game, and gathering fruit. In the days of the Mwami, they had an unique relationship with their Tutsi masters, serving with extraordinary loyalty as the royal hunters, as court jesters, entertainers, messengers, spies, or even as torturers and executioners. Now, with forests rapidly disappearing to make way for the rapidly expanding Hutu and Tutsi population and their many cattle, a number of these relatives of the Zaire forest pygmies had settled to being pot makers and . . .

Richard smiled to himself. Hutu and Tutsi cattlemen still depended on the Twa. "Kill an animal from your own herd?" His thoughts blocked. "Unheard of." A cow was like a mother who nourished you. You couldn't kill her. In the old days, when the people wanted beef, they would go to their local diviner about some problem. After consulting the entrails of a chicken—or performing some other wizardry to find the cause of their latest trouble—he would order the sacrifice of a cow. The Twa were the slaughterers. A tiny piece of meat placed in the roof of the spirit hut was enough to satisfy the ancestors, and the rest would be for a village feast. These days, beef was still a favorite food. Since a cattleman couldn't butcher one of his own animals, he would first sell her to another rancher, then, if need be, buy her back and call a Twa hunter to do the necessary.

Though continuing a peaceful, symbiotic relationship with the others, the Twa still generally held themselves apart from the Hutu-Tutsi culture, refusing to be bound to their modern ways, and for this reserve they were looked down upon by both, considered unintelligent, uncultured, and unable to understand either the beauty of having cows in their kraals or the joy of sharing milk from their own herds.

A single shot suddenly echoed along a distant hill. Richard drew a quick breath. Another volley of rapid gunfire followed, and he thought he heard screams but could not tell if they might be from the attackers or the ones being attacked. "Why this?" He addressed his soundless question to the distant sky.

The sun by then had pushed itself up over the rim of the world, its light bathing the drifting smoke with a perverse beauty, and his lips twisted into a semblance of a smile. In the end, perhaps the Twa would prove the most wise and enduring of Rwanda's peoples, for they had also kept themselves separate from the hate that engendered the Hutu-Tutsi wars.

CHAPTER 7

"Has the Time Come?"

The next evening, Richard glanced hurriedly over his shoulder, then slipped from the main road onto the path that led up and around his parents' place. He tapped at the side entrance. Moments later, the metal gate scraped open a few inches. "Richard!" Malachai's look of apprehension softened into one of welcome, and Richard squeezed through the opening.

"Are the parents here?"

"Your mother's in the house." Malachai closed the gate and lifted a heavy iron bar to firm it in place.

Instead of going directly to see his mother, though, Richard crossed to a nearer building, the annex that, as oldest son, he had used for his personal quarters since his years in secondary school. Everything appeared to be as he had left it—his clothes, his books, his grandfather's things. He dropped his bag onto a chair, hesitated, started to pick up the photo album lying on the table, then changed his mind and went out, cutting across the cement-paved courtyard to the main house, a large, comfortable structure that stood as testimony to his father's business successes.

"Mama!" he called to her from the hall, sounding like a small boy who had been purposely hurt by someone he had considered to be his friend.

She appeared, tall, graceful, a flowing patterned cloth looping from her shoulder, her hair shining and swept up as she had always worn it. Smiling, she held her hands toward him, and he reached out to touch her upper arms, leaning forward to brush his cheek against hers, first on one side and then on the other, in the gentle Rwandan embrace. "Mother." He mouthed the word softly, as if speaking his regret at not having spent more time with her since coming from the university.

"My son." She motioned him toward the living room. "Have you eaten?" She spoke as she would speak on any normal day. "There's milk. And sweet potatoes. And Malachai has set beans to stew."

"Milk." He forced a smile, though his stomach stiffly refused the idea of his putting anything into it, and after she had brought the milk in his own wooden cup, which she still kept with the others in the kitchen, she came to sit with him.

"What's the news of Frank?" she asked at last.

"Gone." Richard's eyes registered what he did not want to have to say. "When I got up this morning, his domestic couldn't tell me where he might be. When he didn't return, I supposed that . . . uh . . . he had gone, perhaps to his Hutu cousins in the south. And I . . . Mama, I wanted to come already yesterday, but . . ." He left the explanation unexpressed. She had heard, as well as he, when the mob had attacked a Hutsi home on the far edge of the settlement past the commercial center, sometime after noon the previous day.

"Malachai spends much of his time in town," she replied.

Clouds passed over the sun just then, dimming the room as if a heavy shade had been pulled. A large kerosene lamp stood on the table for use in the evening, and though a light fixture had been wired into the ceiling, the power that was to have arrived in town the previous year had come no farther than the communal office buildings.

"Several families have, I believe, tried to find their way to some safer area. The others . . ." She paused. "Malachai is doing his best to find out what is happening so he can tell us in advance what *they* are planning."

Even though she did not explain, Richard understood that *they* referred not to the other families but to the interahamwe mobs that had now grouped in their own commune. Extremists claiming they were avenging the death of the president manipulated that excuse to their own political purposes. Everyone was afraid. Not only the Tutsis, but also Hutsis and Hutus. The charge *collaborator* or *accomplice* or *traitor* could be pointed at anyone, regardless of tribe. And there were those who did not fail in using this opportunity to settle old grudges between families. The mobs, having already tasted blood, were easily turned toward new victims, while the one insinuating the accusation could sit back, hands neatly clean. Individuals were targeted and their families destroyed as well so no witness would remain to point out the killers. After he had finally reached home during the cease-fire after the original FPR invasion in 1990, Richard and his parents had discussed the measures to take should their home ever become endangered by the war.

"Go to a foreign country?" his mother had asked then.

"Yes, Mama," he had replied. "If we're obliged to flee, would you be able to live in a refugee camp?"

No matter how he had approached the subject, she had remained quietly adamant. "I couldn't think of that," she had repeated time and again, and somehow he felt that she was restrained by thoughts of those earlier years she had lost on the other side of the border. On the other hand, he saw her attitude as part of her heritage, of her Tutsi dignity. "For myself," she said, "I prefer to die in my own home." That was the Tutsi way, to stand bravely and, if need be, to die honorably where one belonged and not to be caught fleeing pell-mell like a frightened animal. "In any case," she was saying, "I've brought you, my children, into the world. I've educated you and raised you. For me, that is enough. This has given me great joy, and I am content. I want you to do whatever you must do to save yourselves, but as for me, I can never leave. All I ask is that you be my children, that you remember what you have been taught, and that you never forget me."

Now Richard struggled within himself against the numbing and unspoken question: "Has that time come?"

"Regardless of his place in society, Malachai is a man in whom we can trust," his mother was saying. "He's been a very loyal and trust-worthy helper for your father, and before that, for your grandfather. He'll take care of us."

"Of course he will, Mama." Richard spoke automatically.

The clouds suddenly loosened hold on their accumulated moisture, throwing it down, pounding it so loudly on the metal roofing that they could no longer make themselves heard. They each lapsed into a private world, separated by the driving din above. Momentarily, Richard nursed the futile hope that the storm would continue forever and imprison the maddened riffraff who were already gloating over having purged the community of certain marked traitors, and his eyes traced the edges of a slightly lopsided woven disk hanging on the wall opposite where he sat. Faded purple letters worked into the light tan background spelled out the French wishes for a *Bonne Année*.

"Happy New Year."

Silently he regarded the message that mocked the reality of the year that had begun with such hope. It had been fashioned, he supposed, in some earlier year by one of his younger sisters. Many girls of both tribes still learned the intricate skills of weaving and beading, arts that in earlier days had belonged only to Tutsi women, marking them as the elite having no need to sully their hands with lesser occupations. He assumed, though, that a majority of the young women of the new generation relied on others' talents and purchased the baskets and wall decorations that they would bring with them as part of the expected trousseau on their wedding day. No matter how many times he asked, Aline stubbornly refused to let him know to which group she belonged. Though it really didn't matter, the traditional part of him wanted her to have learned and to have the patient skill required to do the beautiful weaving so valued in all respectable Rwandan homes.

"You'll just have to wait to find out," she had repeated every time he had asked.

"And now? With this? How long will that have to be?" Face braced against his hand, he realized that he had begun staring into nothing-ness. Abruptly, he shifted position and with the movement took notice of the large baskets balanced on their woven doughnut-shaped stands in the corner, past his mother's chair. Most of them had been there since they had moved into the house, and they still looked good.

Fine, soft reeds, similar to those that had lined the houses of the ancient Mwami, covered most of the baskets. Held in place with thousands and thousands of fine stitches, they layered the exteriors in long diagonals through which decorative geometric designs had been drawn with purple or black or green-dyed strands. Some, his mother had made herself. A few tiny baskets sat on the bookshelf—sets of five, actually, the sort tourists liked, which nested one inside the other, the smallest hardly more than thimble size. Their conical lids sloped up into long, narrow points, miniatures of those on larger baskets made for carrying bananas or sorghum or other gifts when one went to visit. Fine, dark threads traced neat designs into the stiff, tightly woven walls. Rwandan women had long been classed with the best basket makers in Africa.

Beside the baskets lay three lances, their short staffs beaded with painstaking geometric designs combining red and yellow and blue. Someone had hand stitched them too, maybe his mother or one of his sisters. *Beautiful*, he said to himself, admiring delicate beading and how it offset the ironwork. *Our heritage.* The symbolic implication of these copies of their old-time weapons suddenly caught his imagination. "Huh-huh-huh." Though swallowed into the overpowering pounding of the rain, the sound of his half-laugh echoed sinisterly in his own ears. The double-edged spearheads protruding from the delicate beading, prongs hooking forward and aft, were designed to rip mercilessly through their victims.

The downpour passed too quickly, leaving them in sudden silence.

"My child, remember that when the time comes and I am no longer here, it is you who I am leaving behind to care for your little sisters." His mother's words bridged this new quiet. "Watch over them. Never let them become careless of their dignity."

It was as if . . . "No, Mama," his emotions wanted to shout. "Don't talk like that. What's happening isn't real. We're not in any danger." But his face, his bearing revealed nothing of his feelings. Rwandan mothers always aspired for their daughters. In their society, any girl who behaved carelessly was a shame and directly disgraced her mother. In ancient times, girls who brought a child into the world out of wedlock were banished, if not put to death. Even in modern times, their family's reputation suffered disgrace.

"I'm counting on you, my son."

"I understand, Mama."

"We're Finished"

Darkness fell again—at last. Richard sat leadenlike in his chair, alone in the room. The kerosene lamp on the table beside him flickered across the photo album now open on his knees. He flipped through its plastic pockets, turning past photo after photo, seeing but not seeing. Pictures of Aline that he had taken. Pictures she had taken of him. Pictures of the two them together, of the two of them with Cyusa and Sylvie, of Aline with Lydia, with others, and then he stopped. He let the album drop open to a single picture.

They had strolled through the forest that day. He and Aline. Was it two weeks ago? Only? It seemed like an eternity. Something that had happened in another world. Just the two of them. On the way back, he had stopped her in front of the bougainvillea hedge and snapped the picture. Sunshine. Multicolored blossoms. She in her favorite blouse and jeans. It was the last shot on the last roll of film they had had developed before the Easter vacation. His finger traced the outline of her face and then suddenly—for no logical reason and certainly not because he was interested in having an answer—he was wondering if one or two of the younger children were even now still being sent to see to the needs of Olive.

"Stepmother!" The words hissed between his teeth. His father always spoke of her to him as *your aunt*. Aunt! She was no aunt. She was no mother. She was nothing. Only his father's *wife number two*. A miserable woman. "Hutu mur . . ."

Shocked at the intensity of his own passion, he cut himself short. His hands clamped around the edges of the album, and his fingers knuckled into its back. "There are the good and the bad among every tribe." He forced himself to remember his grandmother's calm voice as she had schooled him of an evening. "Honor my memory by respecting every individual for what he does and not because of his ethnic blood."

Yes, Grandmother, he said in his thoughts, and as if to dislodge the feeling of animosity that continued to swell inside him, he regarded the shelf that held his grandfather's flute and tried to remember the throaty, not-quite-half-tones of its rambling melodies, the ones intended to keep intruders at bay. He had never been able to make the instrument sing as his grandfather had, but in a hidden part of his mind he could almost hear its songs. The old man's stool, the one he had always sat on outside the door when he played in the evening, stood on the floor by the shelf. Beside it, leaning into the corner, were his spear and the carved baton, the badge of office that had marked him as chief of their extended family.

But you and I know that woman has never been anything but miserable toward me and Shema and Marie-Pierre. He twisted his thoughts again toward his grandmother's memory. *Miserable and mean. Serves her right to have been cursed by never having any children of her own.*

"Richard?"

He swiveled toward the door, startled by the soft voice, its tone requesting acknowledgment. "Shema! I didn't hear you. Come in!"

His sister, the child who had come next after him, was his self-appointed caretaker. Usually self-confident and smiling, she seemed now to slink toward a chair. She had lost weight, he could tell, and her face looked drawn and much older. "Studying Aline's pictures again?" The forced playfulness made her question sound stilted and unreal. "You know what I've always told you."

KILL THY NEIGHBOR

"In four months, Aline will be my wife." He, too, tried to assume a teasing tone. "Then who will you have to boss around and take care of and fuss over?" The moment he said that, he felt sorry, for she slumped down even farther, and a chalky gray pushed under her chocolate complexion, dulling it.

"Oh, Richard!" She clenched and unclenched her hands. "How can you talk like that when this is the end for us?"

"There's no need to speak in such an exaggerated fashion. Papa has many friends. Good friends."

"What do you even know about anything?" she retorted. "You're always too positive. What can friends do for us now? This time, nothing will stop them. All the hate. The murdering. Today." Her voice suddenly choked. "Marie." She laced her hands so tightly together that her nails became a ghastly tan-gray. "Innocents like Marie? The devil and all his angels in hell would be easier to stop than those maniacal murderers. Look at me, Richard! Look! What do you see?" Her voice became more shrill. "Look at yourself!" She loosened her hands and flapped one in his direction. "All they'll see is your handsome nose. Your handsome Tutsi nose. I tell you, my brother, I don't know if it'll be tonight. Or tomorrow. But we're finished. Our family is finished."

Her outburst hit him like hard, hot punches, but he let her go on, hoping that her frightened words would help to cleanse away some of the fear that pushed her to talk like this. At last she lapsed into silence.

"It's all right, Shema." He tried to be reassuring. "You'll see. This will pass. It will be as Imana wills. In a few days, the army will settle everything, and you'll be able to go back to your campus in Kigali. I'll go to Butare. We have our cards."

"Our cards!" she interrupted. "Richard. Where have you been these last days since the president was killed? Our cards don't mean anything anymore. If you look like an inyenzi traitor, that's who you are."

Richard sighed. "You'll always be who you are on the inside." And now he was speaking quietly, as a man who was master of his world. "Remember our grandmother. And our mother. They've both taught us the dignity of being who we are." He glanced around the room as if looking for something. "I'm not sure what you plan to do tomorrow," he said at last, "but as for me, I intend to get ready to go back to Butare, and for that I'll need to have my shirts washed. Maybe if you could do that for me tonight, then tomorrow . . ."

"Sure, Richard," she said, as if glad for something to keep her hands busy and to divert her mind from the horror that lurked just beyond the walls of their father's house. "I'll do that for you."

CHAPTER 9

Bwoba

When Shema left, Richard tuned his radio to RFI and picked up the album again. But he neither heard the newscast nor saw the pictures.

"The end! This is the end for us!" What Shema had said was not real. Nothing was real. Not the killing. Not the president's death. Not the mobs. The album slipped from his hands and dropped to his knees. A sharp sound snapped in the distance. He jumped. That was real. Too real. "Finished!" Her ominous predication threatened now to become his. "NO!" he almost shouted aloud.

"Richard?"

In the distance, he seemed to hear someone calling.

"May I come in to listen to the news with you?"

"Oh!" He shook his head as if to clear his thinking. "Sure." It was Robert, his youngest brother.

They sat, listening, and Richard tried to focus on those faraway reports about the massacres, about the mobs with their machetes and clubs and guns pushing over the hills and through the valleys, even at that very moment adding more bodies to those that already bloodied the ground and clogged the rivers of their beautiful little country. "Like it's not real,"

Robert was saying when that part of the news was finished. "Like it's happening in Bosnia. Or Somalia. Or somewhere else and not here."

Richard nodded.

"But it is here. And today . . ." Robert's voice rose into the high tenor that belonged to his age, and he turned his eyes, dull and opened too wide, toward his oldest brother. "Richard?"

"Yes."

The boy hesitated momentarily. "Doesn't it make you afraid? Don't you think something might happen to us?"

Richard drew a long breath. He could hear the newscaster talking about a new variation in economic measures being taken by the world bank, but he neither noticed nor cared what they were. At the same time, he became aware of how the lamplight washed over his brother's profile, and he was struck with how much the boy looked as he imagined himself to have been at the same age—slender, with the ungainly long legs that come at the beginnings of growth into manhood; narrow, pensive face; finely sculpted nose; dark, soft-chocolate complexion; and a slow smile that, when it happened, lightened his entire being and easily erupted into laughter. Yes, in looks they strongly favored each other, and like Shema, they were definitely children of their Tutsi mother.

"Remember the story of Bwoba," Richard finally said.

"That is a story which I do remember."

The way the boy pronounced his answer revealed to Richard that he was using all the skills from their mother's teaching to master his young emotions. And again Richard thought of his own boyhood. He did not know from what era the story of the fearful Bwoba and his encounter with the buffalo had come except that it had to be some time long after the Hutus and Tutsis had settled the country. As a youngster he had tried to imagine the wild openness of the land when the Tutsis arrived with their herds searching for good pasture land sometime in the fourteenth or fifthteenth century, as historians presume, or perhaps earlier, coming from the upper Nile region. Tall, aristocratic warriors with advanced fighting skills, they convinced the Hutus that Imana had sent them to be the rulers. Though fewer in number, they gradually established a feudal-type class system over which their Tutsi Mwami ruled.

In this complex hierarchy, not only did the lords rule their vassals, but cattle chiefs collected tributes in livestock, land chiefs collected agricultural produce, and military chiefs carried out cattle raids as well as fighting wars. Frequent conflicts also raged between them and the kingdom of Burundi to their south. Intrigue and killings among power-hungry contenders for one or another of the lucrative top positions bloodied the history of both countries, and animosity between the two rival kingdoms was so deep and long-standing that both refused the United Nations call for them to form a single state at the time of independence.

Rwanda itself was divided into districts that were divided into *imosozi* (hills) with hill chiefs, which were again divided into neighborhoods with subchiefs. Chiefs of the most important districts formed the Mwami's advisory council. Most administrative posts were held by Tutsis, while the masses of common people, both Hutus and Tutsis, subsisted as mere vassals. Tutsi vassals were given honorable supervisory tasks or were engaged as body servants and child tenders or beer makers and could more readily earn the cattle, which, in turn, would make them lords over others. The Hutus were assigned the heavy work. They were the cultivators, the burden bearers, the ones whose strong shoulders were made to carry the riding chairs of their overlords and members of their households and who were forced to carry out the detestable duty of guarding the overlords' enclosures during the night. Vassals of both tribes tended cattle.

Into this society, Bwoba was born. As had his father before him, he bound himself to work the fields of his overlord. His unhappiness with his life was made even worse because he was a very fearful man. He was afraid of everything. Even the sudden sound of a leaf rustling against the grass was enough to send him running for safety. One day as he was digging in the fields of his master, he heard a big rustling sound. He jumped and looked around. And saw a huge black animal. Its wide, muscular shoulders and heavy, crooked horns pushed through the bushes and into the clearing.

A buffalo!

Now anyone who has even a grass stalk of common sense knows that an African buffalo is something to fear, especially if it is alone, for it is one of the strongest and most dangerous of all African animals. And of all the African buffaloes, the largest and most fearsome are those that are found in Rwanda. When Bwoba saw the buffalo, he did not grab his spear to protect himself should the buffalo charge. He did not look for some other weapon. He did the only thing that his fear told him to do. He ran.

When Bwoba ran, the buffalo also ran. After him.

Bwoba ran faster and faster. Toward a tree.

The buffalo charged after him. Toward the same tree.

Bwoba reached the tree.

The buffalo pounded in close behind him.

Bwoba caught a branch and swung himself up.

Just below him, the buffalo snorted.

Bwoba grabbed another branch. And pulled himself up. Branch after branch after branch. He climbed and climbed, faster and faster, until he reached the very top of the tree.

The buffalo snorted and pawed the ground and shook his horns against the tree. That made Bwoba even more frightened. He became so very frightened then that he did not realize he had reached the very topmost branch of the tree, so he continued to climb, hand over hand over hand and up and up and up into the empty air. Until . . .

Crash after crash he fell down and down through branch after branch after branch. Then . . .

Whomp!

He landed.

Hard.

Smack on the back of the angry buffalo.

The buffalo ran.

"Yiiyiiiyiiiiyiiiii!" Bwoba cried. He was now more frightened than he had ever before been in all his frightened life. He grabbed out and, as if by accident, he clasped onto the long, heavy, curved horns of the buffalo.

The buffalo ran faster. And faster. And faster yet.

Bwoba clamped his knees around the buffalo's back. He gripped the horns, holding them tighter and tighter. He was so frightened he could hardly breathe. He was very, very, very afraid. What if he should fall? He was too afraid to even call for help.

And then he discovered something.

If he pulled on one horn, he could make the buffalo turn in that direction. If he pulled on the other, the buffalo would go in the other direction. So he began to pull on first one horn and then the other. And he began to make the buffalo go in the direction he wanted him to go.

My, thought Bwoba, forgetting his fright, *just wait until I tell my friends about this!*

"When Bwoba fell into that situation and grabbed his enemy by its horns," Richard was saying to Robert, "that's when he realized that he did not have to be afraid."

"But the Interahamwe. Richard? If they come?"

Richard carefully turned his little brother's question over in his mind, looking through his own fears for the best answer that would help the boy calm his. Just then, someone began banging on the gate.

"Hide!" he hissed.

10

The Will of Imana

"Elements!" Malachai grunted. His lantern swung a large gray-yellow oblong across the cement, transposing his husky silhouette into a shuffling giant who stalked the reed-matted hedging. The hedge itself, pencil brush strung through with barbed wire, protected the family holdings as solidly as any brick wall. Should anyone foolishly try to push through, the brittle, pencil-shaped foliage snapped easily, discharging a milky ooze that, especially around eyes, burned with the intensity of hot coals. "Banging on the gates of innocents. Yelling. Running away." Malachai's worn sandals scuffed against the cement, creating a metered sound trail toward the cattle shed, while the swinging of the lantern threw his shadow even larger.

"Malachai?"

The man froze midstep.

"They're gone?"

"It's you? Richard? Yes. It was no one."

"You're going to the cows?"

"To see that their bedding is sufficient." Malachai spoke as though this action on his part should be taken as a matter of course.

KILL THY NEIGHBOR

"I'll come too." Richard let his footsteps blend with the older man's, and his taller shadow became one with the dim gray monster moving along the hedge. They entered the shed. "You've always been so good with cattle." Richard's fingers scratched methodically through Intabanzirwa's coarse dull-cream hide, separating the bristly hair, then smoothing it, and his words seemed to be addressed toward the cow's large, oblong ear rather than to Malachai, who suddenly seemed preoccupied with re-arranging a section of the long-dry grass bedding with his feet. The lamplight now cast a shadow across the ample face, flattening the already-wide nose even more and accenting the heaviness of the jowls. To Richard, this one who lived with their family, tending the cows and seeing to the cultivation of their fields, was more an elder brother than servant. "Was there news in town this evening?" His voice rasped, coming out as hardly more than a whisper. In the background, he heard the muffled scraping of the back door of the house opening and then closing.

"The news continues." Something on the floor seemed to demand Malachai's total concentration.

"And in that news was there anything that . . ." Richard suddenly had no interest in finishing his question. Yet at the same time he wanted to know; he had to know.

"This afternoon it was the family of Evariste."

Richard swallowed hard. "Evariste?" Evariste was another Hutsi. Another dealer in sorghum. A man whose progressive outlook had enabled him to rise above the simple country home that had once belonged to his family.

Malachai continued to regard the floor. "There is no pity." He paused. Toed some more of the dry grass. " 'Go to so-and-so's,' they say. 'Search out so-and-so.' " Abruptly he straightened, his powerful shoulders standing like a block between Richard and the world that lay outside and beyond the hedge. "Everyone has suddenly become Inkotanyi! And the ones who are doing this don't know innocent from enemy." His burly hands fisted.

"But this will soon pass," Richard heard himself saying. "The political leaders will see that they must calm . . ."

"Leaders!" Malachai interrupted. "Them? When they're using the drunk ones. They won't stop till . . ."

Richard felt a sudden straitjacketing, another tightening of that heavy, dull sensation that had become a part of all his waking moments. It wasn't like the pounding-in-his-chest fright that had hit him when whoever it was had banged on the gate. The yelling. The oaths. The crude untruths. He and the entire family had scattered into a panic of instant hiding wherever space could be found to push their persons out of sight. What he felt now was solid, something that wouldn't go away and that held him grounded while the savage events, like a slow, ominously knotted noose, tightened around their very place of dwelling.

"But, of course," Malachai quickly corrected, "your father has earned the respect of everyone and . . ."

"With you here, we of course have nothing to fear." Again Richard heard his voice speaking from a distance, and a part of him almost believed that the brawny, solidly built Hutu who for so many years had faithfully served their family could single-handedly hold back any attackers, that he would stop anyone who would dare try to touch their house. Malachai himself had no worries of ever being mistaken as a Tutsi collaborator, for in looks and action, he was Hutu pure and thorough. In fact, many disregarded his simple personage, since one who could not father children had no standing in the society.

Malachai moved across to another of the cows, and Richard left him to his work and went to the house. He found his mother in the living room, alone, sitting in the light of a small stub of a candle. "I think it would be better if I were to return to Butare." He slipped the idea in as another small piece of simple conversation. "Tonight." He rubbed his hand across the solid plush of the couch where he sat.

"Perhaps you should rather wait to see how events will work themselves out."

"Since they have always kept the campus neutral, I was thinking that it may be an advantage for me to go without further delay and drive there. . . ."

"Certainly not in your car!" Her voice broke with a sudden,

uncustomary sharpness.

"But, Mother, I do have all the right documents." He did not have to say that he referred specifically to his identity card, which proved the Hutu side of his parentage. "I'll be fine."

"Not now!" she warned. "You wouldn't get a hundred meters."

Richard sighed. "Perhaps there is reason in what you are saying." As well as all Tutsis and anyone resembling a Tutsi being targeted by Hutu militia, Hutu males not staying in their home areas to back up a possible military offensive against the FPR were considered as deserters and could be executed on the spot by the militia. In addition, FPR patrols who also roamed the region turned on any card-carrying Hutu. "But I have friends who'd help me." He started to argue, then abruptly broke off, saying, "Though if you think it's better, I'll wait." He did not add what was really in his mind, that instead of going directly to the university, he would cross over into Tanzania and wait there until the government had mastered the situation. "The military, of course, will have everything under control in a few days. Then I'll go."

She nodded. In the dim light, her face looked very drawn. Since Thursday, she hadn't ventured beyond their walls. His father, too, stayed close to home. The six days spanning the gaping interval since the death of the president had each seemed more than a millennium long, and in that time, the bar had not been opened, though his father did go there and to his depots, possibly more out of habit than anything, and the need to keep himself busy. His truck and Richard's car had also stayed solidly parked in their usual place in the yard.

"We'll all be fine, Mama." Richard hoped she found reassurance in his words.

"The will of Imana will be done."

He couldn't tell if she meant to agree with him or if it was her indirect manner of expressing the fatalism of their people and encouraging him to accept the inevitable, should events turn against them.

Shots echoed and vague screams clawed in at them through the heavy darkness. Both sat as though they did not hear, but Richard had the sensation of his body being further squeezed by that suit which even now was shrinking smaller, binding his muscles into themselves and endeavoring to cut off his circulation like some giant pressure cuff. Yet that did not completely explain the reason for his making no move to leave the house and go to his own room. Sitting across from her, simply being with her—somehow he felt almost as he had on the first time that she had visited after . . .

My mother. Deep within himself, he repeated the words he had one time hurled in defiance at his grandmother, only now he caressed them with the respect of an adult who knew the reality of how much he owed to the person to which they belonged. *My mother.* He said them again to himself, yet outwardly he showed no sign of what was on his mind or of his resolve that never, ever, under any conditions, would he allow anyone to take Aline away from him in the way his mother had been taken from his father. The candle's teardrop flame suddenly flared, as if gulping largely from the clear liquid pool into which the stub had melted. In the sudden brightness, he saw his mother smile. And he traced that smile with his eyes, even as he had traced a very similar smile on that long-ago afternoon of her first visit.

CHAPTER 11

"My Mother!"

"What is it, my child?"

Hunched against the weathered reed fencing, Richard continued to stare into some far-off unknown, skinny arms laced around his legs, drawing them upward until his dusty knees knobbed against his chin.

"What makes you ignore the greeting of your old grandmother?" Behind her, smoke filtered through the thatch of her kitchen, adding to its indelible off-gray, and floated in a vague cloud above the round, mud-daubed hut. Half a dozen chickens pecked through the dust outside the open door, searching for kernels that she might have let fall. The old woman studied the boy. "What is it?" she insisted.

"My mother!" The words spurted out in a sharp treble as if the stopper holding them in place had suddenly popped loose. "I want to know the reality about my mother!"

"Your mother?" His grandmother appeared to take a quick step back, and color heightened the weathered skin sagging over her cheekbones.

"My mother!" With a quick hoist of his skinny legs, he stood and crossed his arms tightly against his chest. He looked up, his narrow face intense. "I want you to tell me everything about her. It's today or

74

never. And if you don't tell me, I'm going to go look for her."

"My little one, my son that I love." The woman chose her words slowly. "What is it that your grandfather and I have not done for you? How is it that you must speak to me so? Be patient, and use your wisdom in this matter. You mother will come when . . ."

"This sort of moralizing has gone far enough!" Richard's hands fisted, though by habit he carefully maintained a posture of respect and did not let his fists fall into sight. "It's easy for me to know that she's gone, but I need to know where to and why she had to go."

"Why this troubling of your grandmother, young man?"

Richard shifted, startled by the sudden gruff question.

"This little baboon!" His grandfather's derisive shouting of the term that must never be turned against any human pounded past him and toward his grandmother. "Has he insulted you? Or perhaps he doesn't wish to help Malachai with the cows today? Tell me what's going on between the two of you. I'm fed up with such carryings-on in my home, and I'm disgusted by your constant fretting."

Richard stood as quiet as a statue as the words rained down around both of them, but his mind raced.

"What I would like to know is, who is in control of my household? If it's someone else, I certainly would like to know about it. Otherwise, you have gone past your limits."

The grandmother fixed her husband with a look that years of living together had taught him to understand. "It would be better in this case if you addressed us with discernment and understanding," she murmured.

"Who's giving the orders here?" shot back the old man. "Is it me? Or is it you?"

"Grandfather!" Richard's tongue was suddenly loosened again. "You've talked for a long time now, and I suppose you have finished. If not, it's too much!"

"Oh, I see that you're starting to show your manhood." His grandfather's tone curled with mock surprise. "In our day, it was necessary to have permission to address one's elders. Apart from that, have you fed the cows?"

"Leave the child," warned his grandmother. "He knows how to tend to his chores."

Sensing his grandmother's support, Richard stood his ground and attempted to strengthen his case. "Even if that isn't so," he blurted back, "you're well able to take care of your own business!"

"What have we done to deserve such impertinence from this little babbler who won't give up?"

"It's my right to demand my due." Richard stood his ground.

"It's better if you leave us." His grandmother spoke quietly, her words carefully chosen to convey more to her husband than she actually said. To Richard's surprise, the old man did withdraw, and instead of insisting that Richard be punished, he was shaking his head as if he could make no sense of what was going on.

"And now, my son, my work is waiting." His grandmother's voice had taken on a warning edge. "As for the story of your mother, you'll hear that one day. For now, I can only tell you that it is very long."

"All right," Richard quickly agreed, and then as if in an effort to prove a maturity beyond his age by an aptness in turning words in the manner so valued by the Banyarwanda, he hurried on to say, "but, Grandmother, it's exhausting to live without having a real past, so I'll remember your promise and expect that at the next occasion it will be told to me. And believe me, even if it is too long, I presume that everything will be put to me clear and straight for the interest of everyone concerned. If not . . ."

At that point, with a meticulously modulated tone, his grandmother brought him to the understanding that his words had come to the point where they wavered precariously close to falling over the limits that had already been severely stretched on his behalf.

He inclined his head to show that he understood. She turned, eclipsing into the sobriety of the dignified elder woman that she was, and he hurried out of the yard and down the path to meet Malachai and help him bring in the cows.

12

She Had No Choice

"Richard!"

With a quick scoop of his right foot, he caught the underside of his *umupira*, the ball he had twisted together from the dried banana leaves he had stripped from some of the old plants that still stood on the other side of the enclosure. He had been kicking it against the wall of the granary, and now he flipped it into a high arc, catching it with his knee and bouncing it up into his hands.

"Find your grandfather's pipe for him, would you?"

All morning, his grandmother had scuffled between kitchen hut and house and roost and granary and back to the kitchen, an old woman looking like any other of the many old women in their commune, with a cloth of nondescript origin knotted around her hair and an old wraparound gathering her drooping yellow blouse against the waist that had long outlived its usefulness in bearing more children. She worked as if by rote, paying no notice to her chickens nor to her pair of fat, mottled Muscovy ducks nor, until that sudden request, even to Richard. He dropped the ball and scurried toward the house. She seldom asked for him to bring his grandfather's pipe. When she did . . . "My son, take it to your grandfather," she instructed when he held it out to her, "then come back to me."

His grandfather sat on his stool in his usual place near the edge of the shade from his favorite tree, his floppy-brimmed hat catching the afternoon sun and throwing a shadow over the old cloth draping his shoulders and onto the lap of his dull, plaid wraparound. The pipe the boy carried to him was not just any pipe. It was a smooth, rich gray, carved from the horn of a cow. Cupping the polished bowl in his right hand with the stem curving outward, he lay his left hand politely on his right forearm as he extended it toward his grandfather.

The old man grunted, as if at the moment, words were too precious to be wasted on the boy, and Richard turned and hurried back to his grandmother.

"I've been reasoning through that problematic situation you posed to me and . . ." She spoke toward the ground more than to him and pointed to a mat shaded by the thatch overhang. Richard settled himself across from her. "I've decided that now is the time to sketch out certain milestones for you, but as preamble to what I have to say, I am going to ask you to prove to me your maturity."

Though her words focused on his person, she now seemed to be regarding some point in the far distance, and in the momentary silence into which she lapsed, he studied her face. It was old, very old, but it was the most kindly face he had ever seen, for she was a good mother to him. Her hair was brushed back and up. He liked it better on those special feast days when she wore the golden band stripped from the interior of the sorghum plant, binding it around her hair as did all women who were married and had become mothers of children, and when she tied on one of her newer cloths like the one she wore on the Sundays when she took him across the hill to their little parish church. On those days, she looked less old, and he was proud to go with her.

"If your subsequent comportment ever displays an attitude that is not suitable in our society, I shall be very disappointed." She fixed him with her eyes now, and he looked into their brown depths, noting that the years had not removed their gentleness. "Never forget that, because the world could become very hostile in regard to me if you should ever be classed among children with a bad upbringing. You are aware, aren't you, that the character of a child reflects the education given him by his mother, and in that consideration, our immemorial ancestors have left us with the proverb that says, 'The bad child belongs to his mother.' Therefore, in exchange for what I am about to tell you, you must guard in your memory that anything negative which you might do in the future will fall on my reputation as the mother who has educated you and that you have a responsibility of great magnitude regarding my social position in the ranks of the educators."

Richard twisted impatiently, and before she could continue with further explanations that would delay her voicing what he had waited so long to hear, he quickly said, "Mother, thing promised is thing accomplished. I swear that you'll never be derided because of anything I do. I'll remain a witness to that, because what I want more than anything is to be able to grow up in the reality and the truth about myself." He sat straighter, as if in so doing she would be impressed with his sincerity. "Just tell me, why don't I ever see my mother here? Where is she?"

His grandmother seemed to take forever before she replied and, then, as if in the far distance, he heard her say, "Your dear mama left long ago, when you and your sisters were very, very small, and if you could only understand the pain and the regret we experienced on the day she had to leave. She's such a talented, generous mother, a person without many equals, if you ask me."

"Talk, Grandmother! Tell me what happened!"

"Well, your father met your mother under conditions that for me were totally unheard of. When he told us of this lovely creature he had discovered, your grandfather and I were very concerned about this new way of doing things that was invading our society—and, as we were discovering, our own home. In the past, the parents were the only ones involved in deciding a son's future. In our era, a boy and a girl didn't meet until the day of their marriage. Myself, I didn't know your grandfather before the day my family brought me to his home, yet we accepted each other according to the conditions arranged by our families. Should either of us have refused—well, that would have disgraced both of our families. The only admissible reasons that anyone could accept for dissolution of a union arranged by the parents was the sexual impurity of the woman or the impotence of the man. As for adultery—capital punishment settled that."

This latter information passed over Richard's head as being nothing more than a delaying tactic on her part, and he told her as much.

"My son, be patient during all of your life. Never forget that one who is patient will milk the unbred heifer," she added, lapsing into the Rwandan habit of repeating well-known proverbs to emphasize a point.

"Yes, Grandmother. I'll do that one day."

"Well, your father acted as one possessed, as though some hostile ancestral spirit was leading him to ignore our counsel and to reject our traditions. Your grandfather was as tough then as he is now and tried his best to put an obstacle in your father's way in order to prevent the marriage and the future problems it could cause. The young pair, to which fact you and your sisters bear witness, were not to be dissuaded. Afterward, your grandfather and the other elders began causing trouble for your mother. With the respect that he is given in our community as a solver of problems among the people, how could he allow such a thing in his own household? A woman! Marrying a man of her own choosing! That was going much too far with the modern ideas of liberty and freedom that had taken hold of the young folks, and the elders, in an effort to appease the offended spirits of our ancestors, went so far as to offer them a goat on the young couple's behalf.

"That was not the only problem, though, for in those early days of our new republic there were also ethnic conflicts, to say nothing of the Inyenzi who had fled our country. They had begun slipping in to launch attacks against those who had taken away their power. That fact also caused inevitable trouble for those of your grandfather's sort, and because of all this and more, it was necessary for your mother to find a tranquil shelter elsewhere."

"But where?"

His grandmother seemed not to hear, so he found it necessary to speak again.

"Why meddle with the liberty of my mother? Why wasn't she allowed to stay here with me and my sisters? Didn't you find that wrong at the time?"

"My son, as I've already told you on enough occasions, each person must have his rights within his own culture. On the other hand, people are born into problems that have nothing to do with themselves. As for our society . . ." She interrupted herself to quote another well-worn proverb that in essence said that the family in which the woman has the last word is doomed to destruction. "That shows you to what level we, the women in Rwanda were like slaves—though with certain differences. Even if I see things in a certain manner, I must hold my opinions to myself. As shrewd and as capable and as modern as your mother is, she had no right to any concrete word in family affairs. She had to hold her silence and let the will of her superiors, in her case, your grandfather and his advisors, be done. What is even more regrettable, her own family was also against the marriage of those two young lovers. In brief, the main point of disagreement was the way in which they had gone ahead against the counsel of their families. But worst of all, and the point that complicated the problem to such an extent, was the fact that it was also during the period of ethnic ill feelings. She was forced to leave in the direction of the place where she could find peace of both heart and spirit."

"But where is that?"

His grandmother looked around as if trying to locate the exact direction so she could point it out to him. In that moment, one of the young calves bawled in its pen, and there was a brief scuffling in that direction. The disturbance settled into nothing, and she spoke again. "That is to say that she went to the home of her father and her mother, and according to the last information we had, she left with them for the other side of the border."

Youngster that he was, he suddenly understood the truth of his heritage without her putting it into actual words. His mother was Tutsi.

"When?" Richard persisted.

KILL THY NEIGHBOR

Moisture collected around his grandmother's eyes, and tears began to slide down her weathered cheeks. Her throat worked as she struggled to swallow away her emotion. Finally, she found voice enough to continue. "You were very small, you and your sisters, and with my worn ligaments I, who had already born many children, of whom your father was the last, had to search out how I could again play the role of mother. For that, my solution was found with your grandfather's cows and their milk. With his herds, your grandfather had an enviable social role and, Hutu though he is, he was considered among the ranks of the Tutsis. In respect to that, each morning and evening, I would have to bow before him and offer him butter. To satisfy him in those days, it was necessary to keep lots of milk for making butter, for he liked that very much." "And my father?" Richard interrupted at this new digression. "What's his part in my education?"

"I brought that man into the world," she said with a sigh, "but I swear that since the day your mother left, he has never concerned himself even with those considerations that belong to him. Heart torn by the emptiness of the past and the weight of the impasse of the present and the uncertainty of the future, with his love gone, he passed his days with his calabash of drink. Oh, he still made some pretense of trafficking in rock salt from across the border and selling it to those who had cattle and of taking some interest in the herds that belong to your grandfather. At first, he did not believe that he could ever marry again, but eventually he submitted to the pressure from your grandfather in that too. Your grandfather can never allow his authority as chief of the family to be dominated by the reasoning of this new generation, for as he often says, 'The shoulder can never be higher than the neck.'

"But my mother—why hasn't she ever come back to take me with her? Why hasn't she come to take me away from *her*?" He could not find any word appropriate enough to define the woman who, at his grandfather's insistence, had been brought to his father's house, which stood a scant thirty meters away on the other side of the hedge. As the youngest child, his father had built his own house on the family holdings so he could live by his parents and be there for them in their old age. The woman to whom Richard referred even now flaunted her authority as his new wife. "And you?" Weren't you concerned with this wickedness of a society that separates a child from his mother?" Despite his minimal age, his words flowed with a comprehension born and matured in the intense longing that filled his small being.

"Your mother had no choice. She had to resign herself. When the elders decide, the case is closed, and the ones concerned find themselves in front of an accomplished fact. As for my opinion regarding the judgment of our society and this separating of a mother from her children, I've already given the prevailing situation, and to have gone against what was decided, I would have risked my own life."

"But, Grandmother . . . ?"

He was about to ask her how he himself could fight against this injustice given them by their ancestors, to ask what he could do to fix this thing that had separated his mother from him. But just then, his grandfather's authoritarian voice rose on the other side of the hedge, exercising its sway over some discussion being carried on by a group of men returning from their day's business. "I'll go for water," he volunteered with a sudden wisdom that added momentum to his feet, and getting an earthenware jug, he ran at full tilt out of the gateway, down the path, and toward the distant spring.

CHAPTER 13

Hutus and Tutsis

The moon, an almost-round disk, lay a soft silver-gray matting across the earthen courtyard and stood black silhouettes of the granary and calf sheds against the enclosure. On a distant rise, three trees stretched flat-leafed branches wide under the heaven, as if expecting some gift from the gods to be dropped into them. In the far distance, a muffled *chu-chu-chu-chuh* announced that a hyena had come upon the discards of a lion kill. Like another of the silent evening statues, Richard stood in the doorway, detached only a few paces from his grandfather, who, hunched on his stool, looked like nothing more than another dark hump in the moon-light. The old man played his flute, and the melodies from the bamboo instrument—now twining with the gentle shuffling of the cattle, now soaring high and free—were songs intended to announce the presence of a protector, songs intended to keep the bandits away, songs that, to Richard, seemed to be something his grandfather was hearing from some faraway place and then repeating.

Music of the ancestors, he thought. Briefly he wondered about those long-ago people who had come with their cows to this beautiful land and had handed down the traditions that had left him and Shema and Marie-Pierre to the ugly moods of Olive, their stepmother. "If it weren't for Grandmother . . ."

He heard her moving about in the house. That morning, they had gone, the two of them, to the little church on the other side of the hill, walking side by side, his grandmother with a brightly flowered cloth draping from her shoulders and he in his khaki school shirt and shorts. They had sat on a backless brick pew while the priest intoned words that he did not understand. Somehow the priest and his prayers and the haunting melodies of his grandfather's flute seemed to belong together. And then that afternoon he had seen one of the more-affluent Hutu men walking his cows along the main road, "To show that he has risen in rank to be among the favored," his grandmother explained. "In other years, many men walked their cows on Sunday so their neighbors could see."

He wanted to talk to her about that. She could explain so many things that he thought for sure she was one of the wisest women in the entire commune. From her he had learned that it was to show respect that one greeted others with both hands, that it was good to carry gifts in a covered basket because that creates curiosity, and that for a woman to whistle was not only grossly impolite, but it could cause her husband such bad luck that even his cows might go dry. In addition, she had taught him that he should always politely decline should any family not within their intimate circle invite him to eat with them, that certain tribes living across the border ate grasshoppers and termites and even rats and monkeys, that they themselves had only recently learned from the Europeans to eat chickens and eggs, that women were forbidden to eat goat's meat because that would cause them to grow beards like the goats themselves, and that it was unthinkable for any Rwandans other than the Twa to eat sheep's meat, because those gentle little animals that grazed with their cows provided the skins in which mothers carried their babies on their backs. The list continued. But now he wanted to know about other things. More important things, like about cows and status in the community and about the church and the ancestors. Somehow, all of that seemed to belong together and to be part of this thing called Hutu-Tutsi, but his thoughts would not let themselves be formed into real words. Turning, he went into the house. The weak glow of a kerosene lantern diluted the darkness. "Grandmother?" He spoke softly, tipping the word into just enough of a question so she would know he wanted her to acknowledge his presence and give him permission to speak.

"My child, is it that the cows are already settled and that Malachai has no more need of you?" She replaced the lid on the large, round basket into which she had just rolled the good clothes they had worn earlier that day.

He politely squatted down onto the mat across from her before answering—he would never think of speaking to her while standing when she was already seated, for that would imply that he was more important than she. "Yes, the work for which Malachai has need of me has been finished," he said.

They chatted about certain things of the day that had no special consequence to either, and then when enough time had properly passed, Richard asked, "Can you explain to me the meaning of all this talk about Hutu and Tutsi?"

"That is an important question, my child." His grandmother paused thoughtfully. "A very important question to be sure, and the time has come for you to know the answer. So stay here to listen, for to answer that question, I will begin by telling you a story, and I will reveal the answer to you by means of that story."

Shuffling sounds in the sleeping room told Richard that Shema and Marie-Pierre were still awake—and listening. Storytelling was reserved to the women as part of the education they were to pass on to their children, and, according to their traditions, their stories could be told only after darkness had fallen. "That way, no one can be offended by anything that is said," their grandmother had explained.

"Once upon a long-ago time . . ."

Richard listened as if it were the first time for him to hear about the three children, Kigwa, Mututsi, and their sister, Nyampundu, who by some strange accident one long-ago day had fallen out of their home in heaven and onto this earth.

"When they fell, they carried with them fire, iron, the forge, and cattle," their grandmother was explaining. "In due time, Kigwa married his sister, and from their union came the dominant Tutsi clan of the Abanyiginya, through which the line of descent is traced to Gihange, the founder, the same Gihange who the ancient stories say is the one who led the Tutsi people into present-day Rwanda.

"The Hutus, a strong and courageous people who place great value in hard work and prosperity, already lived in our beautiful hill country, cultivating its rich soil," she continued. "When the Tutsis arrived, the land was not crowded like it has become today, but it was plentiful, with more than enough room for all the people and all their cattle. So the Tutsis stayed and prospered. And they observed with interest how the Hutus lived under the organization of their little kings, whom they called 'the Bahinza.' The people believed these Bahinza were endowed with magical powers and could cause rain to fall and seeds to grow. They also thought they could protect crops from insects and cattle from disease.

"The Tutsis were very impressed with this organization and endeavored to contrive a way of adapting it as their own. 'Imana has given us the right to rule,' their leaders told the Hutus. 'He has given us ownership of all the land and of all the cattle.' "

The old woman's voice continued to rise and fall with the many intonations of their Kinyarwanda language, the language that had come to be shared by all Banyarwanda, including the Twa, a Bantu tongue in which intonation and tonality pervade both grammar and vocabulary and which is richly filled with proverbs and allusions as to how life should be lived. From outside the door, the close-toned rhythms from his grandfather's flute added a pretty background, and in his mind Richard wondered why the old-time people had to be so greedy. He wanted to speak, to ask why, but his grandmother pushed ahead, giving no room for his questions.

"The Hutus envied the Tutsis' herds, for they saw that all the cattle and the milk and butter did indeed make the Tutsis very rich, and they wished to have a part in this wealth. They also felt a certain awe, though it was not lacking in disdain, toward the tall gracefulness of the Tutsi people, whose manner of speaking was very convincing, even as it still is today. In addition to this impressive way of expressing themselves, the Tutsi warriors had developed advanced ways of fighting, which, even as they are still today, were also very convincing—especially to any Hutu group that dared to resist the idea of the Tutsis taking leadership into their own hands.

"Bit by bit, the Tutsis gained control, adapting the system of the Hutu little kings to enforce their power. And above everyone they installed their own supreme king, the Mwami, whom they claimed was *the eye through which Imana, the supreme god, looks upon Rwanda.*

" 'If ever the Mwami leaves the country,' they warned, 'he will take its happiness and its prosperity with him.' " At this point, the woman digressed to make the children aware of their country's present-day situation. "Since power was taken from the Mwami during the time when we were preparing for independence, and he was sent away from our country and taken into exile, we ourselves are tasting the results. The happiness we enjoyed while the Mwami lived in his palace at Nyanza is no longer ours. My children . . ." Though the girls were in the sleeping room, she included them. "The absence of your mother is also due in part to the absence of the Mwami." Then she continued with the story of the past.

"With the Tutsi Mwami in place, the Hutus began to see that much of the happiness and almost all the prosperity belonged to the Tutsis, who claimed that Imana had not intended that they should use a hoe themselves, but instead, he had created the Hutus for that work. And they left all the cultivating and all the heavy work to the Hutus, making them nothing more than slaves in the land that was once their own. To their dismay, the Hutus found that they had become the little people, the workers who no longer had the sort of prosperity that they once valued, and that they were enslaved in a caste system of vassals and lords and subchiefs and chiefs and were subjected to the oft-times cruel whims of their unpredictable masters, whose word was law. As time passed, though, certain of the Hutu vassals were respected and loved by their Tutsi lords and, with the Tutsi habit of giving gifts of herds, which also still remains to this day, they were given cattle by their masters. Becoming owner of this pearl of great value, a herd of cattle, immediately placed the person so honored in the ranks of the rich. Thus they moved up to be among those who were to be respected and regarded as leaders, who could acquire vassals of their own and so be considered as Tutsis.

"This acquisition of his own cows also put the man in the enviable position of being able to marry a Tutsi woman—everyone considered the genteel Tutsi women to be much more beautiful than the hardworking Hutu women—for now he could afford the substantial bride price of cattle that the Tutsis demanded. Otherwise, there was no mixing of the two tribes except in the case of the Tutsi men who took Hutu concubines.

"This standard existed even into the coming of the Europeans— the standard in which the terms *Hutu* and *Tutsi* no longer necessarily referred to bloodlines or tribal groups. A Tutsi was one who owned cattle and therefore belonged to the ruling class; Hutus were the masses of little people, the vassals and the slaves of no matter which bloodline, who owned neither land nor cattle, but lived out their lives working for their lords.

"The European colonialists in many ways profited from the system of the Mwami and his subchiefs to aid in their own ruling of the country, and in the days of the Belgian administrators, all Rwandans were forced to carry identity cards showing their ethnic category. If a person owned herds and was in any kind of administrative post, that one, regardless of his heritage by blood, was inscribed as a Tutsi. Any simple domestic or laborer who did not have the good fortune of owning cattle was classed with that large majority of common people and called Hutu. Among that large group were many Tutsis.

"When stirrings for independence began to seep through our continent, the Hutus—the little people—consolidated to raise this Tutsi curtain that had been imposed upon their liberty, and they struggled for their freedom, not only from the European colonists, but from the oppressive Tutsi rule. The Hutus who won control lived in the northwest of our country in the area of the volcanoes. Through all the centuries, they had stubbornly resisted and had never fully fallen under the domination of the Mwami. Then at independence, instead of sharing their new power with their Tutsi allies, they suddenly turned their shoulders and refused to give them places of leadership. At the same time, this new government kept the old idea of the identity cards, only now they forced everyone to register according to their blood heritage. Despite our common language and culture, our two tribes have many differences, not only in the way we look, but in the way we behave. It was easy for almost everyone to know to which blood group they belonged, and if a person was not ready to say so for himself, his neighbors could easily point it out.

"With their leaders so crudely shut out of power, a band of Tutsi youths attacked a Hutu political leader, who was also one of the few Hutu subchiefs. The next day, false reports saying that he had been killed were circulated. This ignited more clashes between the two groups. The Hutus pillaged and burned Tutsi huts. Thousands of Tutsis fled to the neighboring countries of Burundi, Congo [Zaire], and, from our area, into Uganda. From these refugees came the inyenzi, the cunning and stealthy Tutsi attackers who since that time have been trying to destabilize our new government and bring back the Mwami. In all this fighting back and forth, your grandfather . . ."

The old woman bent forward. "My son," she said, as if he alone were hearing her. "In the past, we had the problem of Tutsi masters and Hutu slaves, but according to me, the problems you see these days, even the problems of your own dear mother, are created by the politicians. They have poisoned the people with these terrible ideas of killing. Always remember, there are bad people on both sides, and there are many good people on both sides. In the past, before we had this modern idea of independence, during a difficulty, anyone, whether Hutu by blood or Tutsi by blood, could call on his neighbor for help without having to make reference to any ethnic etiquette. Even our clans cut across the bloodlines to include all three of our tribes, though with intermarriage being rare in earlier times, this was not a thing of cross-tribal linking, but rather a false way of achieving unity in the country. Do honor to my teaching as your mother, my child, and follow the way of doing good, the way that is taught by the priests in our church, who say that we should love our neighbors as ourselves. Always respect a person for what he is, and not according to the bloodline to which he may belong."

"Yes, Grandmother, I will always remember." In the light of the low-burning candle, Richard met his grandmother's gaze, and his eyes reflected the sincerity of his young heart. "I will never forget."

"Never forget," she repeated. "And you will do honor to my teaching. Tonight I have told you a little of some of the causes for this terrible hate between the Hutus and the Tutsis that relate to the problem of your mother. I also want you to understand that under the Tutsi domination your grandfather was forced as a boy to live without his father, who, much against his will, was retained by the Mwami in the special training place of warriors. The Mwami, as I have told you before, was a person of great power, and his word . . ." Her voice trailed away as though she was thinking of something that she wanted to share and yet at the same time did not want to say. "I remember the story of the Mwami Gahindoro, who ruled long before the time of my own father's grandfather. An enemy had been captured. The Mwami asked his advisors to propose an exquisitely painful way to execute him. When none of the others spoke, the courtesan Kamegeri at last proposed an idea. 'Heat the big, flat rock that looks like a couch,' he said. 'Build fires around it. Heat it hotter than any rock has ever before been heated. Then throw the criminal on that rock, and he will suffer a most terrible death.'

"The Mwami agreed and told Kamegeri to carry out his plan. And so at the appointed time Kamegeri ordered Hutu vassals to tear down all the huts and granaries in the area and to stack all the combustible material around the rock. They lighted a fire, and it burned fierce and hot. When it began to burn itself out, he forced the men to sweep away the debris, which, because of the extraordinary heat, they could do only with extremely long bamboo sticks. When it was cleared, the Mwami, who had been watching, saw the brutally ashen-hot surface. 'Bind him hand and foot,' he cried out, pointing to Kamegeri. 'The inventor of such an atrocious punishment has no right to live.' And Kamegeri was thrown to his death on the cruel rock.

KILL THY NEIGHBOR

"In the old times, being of the ruling class, though giving one an enviable position, also placed one in many dangers. Not only could the Mwami suddenly turn on those who for one reason or another had crossed his temper, but he, as well as all his underling chiefs, had to be on constant guard against power-hungry plotters and assassins. In the case of your grandfather, even though his own mother had Tutsi heritage, the unjust whims of the later Mwami that made his Hutu father a veritable prisoner in the royal warriors' camp went beyond his tolerance. Regardless of the mixed blood that he carries in his own being, he is and always has been more Hutu than Tutsi. The political evolution of our country has been such that those who wish to unite the two sides have always been considered as traitors—a Hutu who gets along with the Tutsis is considered as a traitor by his brothers, and a Tutsi who in any way seems to support the Hutus is considered to have abandoned his side. Those with moderate tendencies have themselves been subjected to a very undesirable fate.

"And so it continues in these times of so much hate, when the life of one on the opposite side has little value. Your grandfather found that the best protection for your mother and for our entire family was to send her to the safety of her own family and her own tribe. The only hope we have is to pray that Imana will look down on us and bless our country with a time of peace and understanding, so that you and your sisters can have your dear mother back."

"But, Grandmother."

He shifted now as he spoke the second question that burned in his young heart.

"Why this other woman who is not my mother? Why did Grandfather insist that my father bring her here?"

14

Man With a Machete

"Richard!"

The youngster stirred, snuggling his thin body against the warm spot on his mat and digging his chin deeper into the ragged edges of his gray blanket.

"The time has come for you to be up!"

"Mmmmgggghh . . ." Richard forced his eyes open and sensed more than saw his grandfather standing in the sleeping-room doorway. *Leave me alone!* his thoughts grumbled in the secret of his head. *Find another slave!*

"If a small bird can't fly, it won't know where the ripe grain is."

Curled under their blanket on the far side of the mat, Shema and Marie-Pierre breathed with the deep regularity of children who have no need to be disturbed from their lost world of sleep. They didn't have to be the object of their grandfather's endless proverbs. They didn't have to get up while it was still too dark. For a long moment, Richard envied his sisters, but he dared not test the old man. Rolling over, he grabbed his shorts and shirt, pulled them on, and stumbled into the fresh predawn stillness. A few splashes of water from the calabash he'd filled the evening before startled his sleep away. At the calf pens, everything seemed to be in order, so he hurried on to rekindle the fire. Malachai lighted it at six each evening, just as the sun prepared to slip through the quick equatorial dusk and into its deep abyss of darkness. The flames, near the entryway and across from the cows' bedding place, held preying animals at bay during the night, softened the chill of early morning, and chased flies until milking was over and the cattle had left for their daytime pasture. Sometimes, though, it didn't hold through the entire night, and thus Richard's first duty was to set it burning again, before the cows could be disturbed by the dip in temperature that often comes with dawn at high altitudes in the tropics. Malachai would begin the milking later.

After the flames settled into a solid blaze, Richard hovered near, soaking in the warmth, oblivious that his tummy bulged through the gap where a button had been torn from his off-olive shirt, oblivious that a three-cornered tear in his shorts framed a patch of his brown bottom, oblivious that their frayed edges dangled too wide around his bare, skinny legs. "Better get more water," he grumbled to himself. "And maybe *she* will stay out of my way."

He didn't know who expected him to work harder—his grandfather or *her!* In his mind, his grandfather was hard, making him responsible for unfair amounts of work with the cows and around the family holdings in addition to having to help his grandmother. "But *she* . . ." He did not want to put a name to that other woman. "Picking on me! Lying about me to Papa." He rubbed his hands up and down his upper arms, remembering the sting from the limber branch that had coiled again and again across his back and around his shoulders the evening before.

"Richard didn't bring wood when I asked."

In his mind, he mimicked Olive's complaining nasal voice.

"He never obeys. Never brings me water!"

"Liar!" he shouted under his breath. "How can Papa listen to her lies? And beat me? For nothing? She's . . ." He clamped his teeth together, biting down until the muscles of his jaw became so hard that they hurt. "She's . . ." He imagined a hundred terrible things, but none of them were bad enough. "She's not my mother!" With a violent hiss, the words exploded between his teeth, and he swiped out angrily with his foot, catching a loose branch and flipping it up and into the flames. "Not my mother!" He stamped his foot down, spun around, and rushed to get a big calabash from his grandmother's stockroom, nearly stumbling over a long, rectangular garden basket sitting near the door. He'd carry water before he had to leave for school, lots of it, for his grandmother, but not a drop would he take to her at the other house where she stayed with his father. Not a drop. How his father could be so . . . so . . .

He could not begin to comprehend how his father had let himself be pushed into marrying this dumpy Hutu woman, this Olive, as they called her, as if he didn't remember he was still married to their mother, and then bringing her to be the mistress of his home, to flaunt herself around as if she were queen of their world, ordering them about like little domestic animals. The fact that his father had built one of the nicest houses in the community—cement floors, plastered walls, tile roof, real windows—made her strut, heavy feet plumping down, head thrown back from her skinny neck like some deranged crested crane.

"Do this! Do that!"

Richard grabbed up a big yellow-brown calabash, the largest and most beautiful, and a head ring. "For Grandmother," he muttered through still-clenched teeth, glad at least for the warmth and the care of the old woman who kept him and his sisters as her own. "If *she* needs water, let her come across and get it from Grandmother."

He hurried out to the road that wound through his grandfather's holdings, past the eucalyptus-bordered pasture where the calves grazed during the day, along the flat stretch where he and Frank sneaked from their after-school herding duties to hold clandestine football (soccer) matches with their friends, and down the slope past banana patches and gardens. He smiled as he passed rows of sweet potatoes, momentarily forgetting about Olive. Just the day before, he and Frank and three of the other herd boys had sneaked into that garden and had found plants with tubers already of an edible size. Digging in, they helped themselves to several, carried them back to the pasture where their calves grazed, dug into the ground, built little earthen ovens, and lighted fires. "Stolen fruit tastes sweetest," his grandfather said. After the excitement of taking the sweet potatoes without being caught and of roasting them, they did indeed taste very sweet. But a part of Richard knew that what they had done was not right, that if his grandmother knew about them taking the sweet potatoes, she would have something to say about the priest and his teaching about loving one's neighbor.

Twenty minutes later, he reached the shallow valley, dipped the calabash into the pool where everyone collected water, and hoisted it, dripping, to his head. The sun had by now climbed into the sky over the distant forest, warming the world, and Richard mounted the slope with sure, quick steps, the calabash riding in easy balance on his head ring of plaited dry brown banana leaves. A pair of glossy ibises alighted in a stretch of pasture, and in the sun their dark backs and wings shimmered with a deep, shiny purple and a glossy green, almost as if they were imbedded with large sequins. He turned his head to watch as they stalked the field, methodically foraging for breakfast with their long, curved beaks.

Just then, something rolled under his right foot.

He stumbled.

The calabash bobbed forward.

He grabbed.

The calabash slipped. It hit the earth with a heavy thud.

With frightened strides, the pair of birds hastily threw their thick, round bodies into the air and beat their wings furiously to gain altitude. But Richard did not notice. All he saw was the water streaming out and swirling dust into little tan islands around his feet.

"Mama! No!"

He stared at the wide crack, that now split the polished gourd, then grabbed it and raced up the hill.

"Grandmother!" he yelled, bursting into the yard and glancing hurriedly around. "Grandmother! The big water jug is broken!" He rushed the words out before he would have to say them to her face.

"What's this?" his grandmother demanded, poking her head around the door. "And why all this crying so early in the morning? You must be more careful! Gourds don't grow on every bush, you know!"

"I'm sorry, Grandmother. I . . ." But he did not want to admit that he had been looking at a pair of birds and had carelessly stumbled on an old corncob. "I'll be more careful," he promised.

"Then take another calabash. We'll need more water before you return from school."

"Yes, Grandmother."

At school, he scooted into place on the mud-plastered brick bench and settled his slate across his knees just as the whistle blew. He tried his best to correctly copy what the teacher chalked onto the black-painted surface covering most of the front wall, but his hand and his mind did not seem to be operating in the same sphere. Everything the teacher said wanted to twist around and thread into the one wish that filled his mind: *I want my mother!* Suddenly a faraway throbbing seemed to pulse out of nowhere and move toward their school. It neared, growing louder. The children began to squirm, turning toward the windows.

"Helicopter!" someone whispered.

An almost-visible shiver swept the entire class.

"Sit quietly." The teacher spoke calmly, though he had to raise his voice to be heard above the motor's din. "There's no need to become alarmed."

The machine roared over them, wake from its thumping motor washing around the school. Richard ducked, thrusting his slate over his head.

"The big turning things cut off Tutsi heads!" Haricot yelled.

Richard turned, eyes pleading with his stocky little Hutu seatmate, who, for some forgotten reason, everyone called 'the bean.' *No!* his thoughts yelled, but he made no sound.

"Yeah," shrilled the voice behind him. "My papa says they chop off their legs too. Chop them all to pieces."

Richard's slate dropped to his knees. He clapped his hands against ears, shutting away the big, horrible noise and the terrible things the boys were saying, and he crouched into a terrified huddle between his Hutu classmates. *No one can do that to my mother*, his thoughts screamed. *Not my mother!*

At the same time, he knew that Hutus and Tutsis were fighting again.

KILL THY NEIGHBOR

That it was still too dangerous for his mother to come back because of the Inyenzi. His grandfather and the other men talked lots about those terrible Tutsi killers. They sneaked in and murdered Hutus. They were wicked! Evil! And the men bragged about what the Hutus would do to those Inyenzi and their supporters—if they ever caught any of them.

And me?

For the first time, that little question slipped into his mind. His thoughts suddenly froze. He knew he was Hutu because of his father. But people said he looked like his mother.

Like a Tutsi?

Waves of the chopping, pulsing din held him immobile, and then the helicopter began to ease away from the school. As if responding to some unheard signal, all the children suddenly pushed toward the row of windows framing the world on that side of the building—and they watched the machine with its whirling wings bob toward the distant hills.

"It's all right, children," the teacher continued, trying to calm their frightened questions. "The new president's just sending it to see that all of us out here in the country are fine." A military coup had made General Juvenal Habyarimana president only a short time earlier. "It's nothing to be afraid of." The helicopter grew smaller and smaller until it and its dreadful noise disappeared. The teacher regarded his nervous charges. "But I think it would be well for you to go home early."

That day, no one straggled. No one stayed to play games or to talk. With legs stretching into long strides, Richard and Frank quickly sorted themselves from the others and sprinted along the narrow path edging a field of sweet potatoes. A huddle of Tutsi children ran ahead. "Do those machines really chop off people's heads?" Richard asked.

Frank grimaced. "They'd have to turn upside down."

Just before they reached the fork in the path that would take them on their separate ways, one of the girls ahead suddenly screamed, "Hutu!"

Richard saw a man running across the field, machete in his hand. "Watch out!" he shrilled, pushing away from Frank. "He's going to get us!"

Without another look, he ran. Feet pounding. Faster. Faster. Footsteps pounded after him. He veered onto a side path, his heart banging in his ears. He dodged toward his grandfather's fields. His chest heaved. His breath gulped in, stinging the back of his throat. He threw himself off the path, through the bananas, toward the back entrance. Then across the yard and into the house. He dove through the door into the sleeping room, scooching along on his belly until he disappeared under a pile of blankets and old clothes.

He heard footsteps.

Someone grabbed at the blankets.

He whirled around, throwing his arms over his head.

"Why this?"

At the sound of his grandmother's voice, he let his hands drop. "A Hutu!" Quivering, he pushed himself into sitting position. "A Hutu," he said again, fighting hard to hold back his tears. "He had a machete!"

The Stranger

Shema and Marie-Pierre trudged after Richard along the path toward the main road. "Teacher's not going to like this." Tears quavered in Marie-Pierre's voice. "She told me not to come late anymore."

"Our teachers'll be mad at us, too, and *she* knows that." Shema spat toward the side of the path as if to clean a bad word from her mouth. "Making us bring wood when she didn't even need it. Making us bring water. Making us do anything, just so we have to be late. *She* is nothing but mean, mean, mean!" She spat again. "And MEAN!"

Richard swung around to face his sisters. "I'm going to go find Mama!"

Marie-Pierre's big brown eyes grew even bigger, and a tear balanced at the corner of one. "Today?"

"Grandmother has told me where to go to find the house of our mama's mama and papa."

"Will you take us?"

Richard shook his head at his youngest sister's questions. "It's very far."

"Aren't you afraid to go by yourself?" the practical Shema asked.

Richard shook his head again. More than two years had passed since the day of the helicopter, when he had run from the man with the machete. For a week afterward, he had hidden at home, afraid to go back to school, but no one had ever seen another trace of the stranger or heard in what direction he had gone. Now he was almost eleven, a little bigger—though everyone said he was too short and too thin for his age—and very much faster. And things were different. Lots of things. "If Papa won't let her come stay with us, then I have decided that it is in our interest for me to go and try to find her. When I find her, I'll ask her if we all can live with her."

"She'll let us come. I know she will." Shema spoke with a nine-year-old's confidence.

"But she belongs here! With us!" Richard's eyes snapped, and a ridge of muscle showed along the line of his jaw. "There's no reason she can't come now, even though Grandmother says . . ."

"In cases such as these, we must be very careful so as not to create problems that we do not need to create," the old woman had sagely cautioned Richard the evening before. "Your mother will come when the time is right."

"But at school they say . . ."

"Yes. They say. It is true that people have many opinions on every subject. But . . ." In the evening darkness, Richard had sensed more than seen the wrinkled hands slide across the worn skirting in the way his grandmother had when she found it necessary to explain things she would rather not talk about, and he could tell that she had nervously gathered a few folds between her fingers and had begun to slowly rub them together. "Even if the new laws do make it possible for our people from both tribes to settle back to living together as they once did and to live again like normal neighbors, one can never be too careful. One can never be sure of what another is thinking. I have told you before, and I will tell you this again: it is best never to put into words what you really think. Remember that the man who is cunning and deceitful earns the admiration of others because our people have learned to believe that the man who tells no lies cannot feed his children. We have our ways, that is to be sure. We may treat a neighbor as a friend; then when he becomes careless in our presence and turns, we are quick to stab him in his back to make gains for ourselves." His grandmother had clucked her tongue then. "I cannot say that this is a good habit—certainly it does not conform with the teachings we learn from our priests at the church—but it is the way of behavior that we have been given by our ancestors. And that is how it is among our people. And because of that . . ."

"But where is she?" Richard had interrupted. "Is my mother so far that she cannot come?"

"Not far in that sense," the old woman replied. "Her home is . . ." And she told Richard the direction and the place. "But, my child, you must guard your patience, for it may still be far in the sense of what has happened."

"Patience! That is all we've ever heard!" Richard exclaimed now to his sisters. "I am tired of all this patience, and I am going to find her. Maybe not today. But I'm going." He stomped his foot down and suddenly became aware of how short his shadow had become under the mounting sun. "We have to hurry!" He swung about. "Maybe if we run, our teachers won't be so mad."

After school he had stayed with Frank to play football as long as he dared; then the two of them left together. The older children were already worrying. Exams, the ones every sixth-grader had to pass in order to get into secondary school, would be set in a few weeks. "Not fair!" Frank had picked up a clod and sent it sailing toward a skinny dog that had run out onto the path after them. The cur let out a mournful yip, and turned, long, narrow tail tucked between bony legs, and slunk toward the hut from which it had come. "Only so many Hutus and so many Tutsis and so many Twas can go. And what do the Twas care?" Frank was a year older than Richard and already in his last year. "They don't even like school. But Tutsis are smart. Lots of them'll pass, and then they still can't go 'cause there won't be enough places. It's not fair!"

Like so many families in this area where the Tutsis had originally established their monarchy, both of Frank's parents were of mixed Hutu-Tutsi heritage. The quota system, though, was based on a presumed population distribution of 85 percent Hutu, 14 percent Tutsi, and 1 percent Twa. With only enough secondary schools for about

10 percent of the children, this severely limited the number of primary-school finalists who could go on to a secondary institution.

"Lucky we're Hutus like our papas, and my papa already says I had better pass that exam next year. Or else." It was hard for Richard to believe that early missionaries actually had to go out and catch children for their schools. His grandmother said she had seen them with her own eyes. White missionaries. Coming into the village. Taking boys. Some parents hid their children, fearful of the poison they said missionaries used to cast a spell over a child so he would no longer follow the way of the ancestors.

"Yeah," Frank was saying. "My papa too. Says he's gonna beat me if I don't make it."

"You'll do fine. You're smart."

Frank grinned, not arguing. "Where do you want to go after?" he asked.

"The Petit Seminaire [Little Seminary]."

"Almost everybody does. Everyone likes their white uniforms, and even my mother points at them and tells me, 'See them, Frank? Now those boys know how to behave. Better than the types from the other schools.'"

"I'm going to wear a white uniform." Richard planted his feet wide in the path and shoved his hands into the shallow pockets of his khaki shorts. "And carry a white school bag on my back."

"Then you have to be a priest."

"That's what Grandmother wants me to be."

It was taken for granted that boys who attended the Catholics' Petit Seminaire would go on to the Grand Seminaire (Big Seminary) and then into the priesthood. In fact, it was taken for granted that students who went on to school would most likely become Christians and belong to the church that operated the school they attended. Most of the country's schools were still mission-operated—most by Roman Catholics, some by Protestants. Early on in their administration of the country, the Belgians had decided to conduct all primary education through missionary schools and in 1930 began subsidizing all Belgian Roman Catholic schools that met educational standards. Then in 1963, shortly after independence, the National University in Butare was established by the government in conjunction with the Roman Catholic Dominican Order of Canada.

"I think I'll be a teacher." Frank spoke decisively. "You don't have to go to school so long."

"Grandmother says that if I don't become a priest, I should be a doctor. Or even a teacher," Richard added generously. "She says they're all good people who help others. If she had her way, everyone would help everyone else, and there would be no more fighting or ethnic problems or anything. But Grandfather thinks I should join the military and become a general with stars on my shoulders."

Both boys had laughed then.

Several Sundays later, while Richard and his sisters were playing in the shade by the calf sheds, a strange woman entered the yard. Tall and slender, she greeted their grandmother with grave dignity. Something about her seemed familiar, yet, as far as he could remember, Richard had never before seen this person in his life. Just then, Olive strode in.

"Richard!" she spoke sharply. "I need . . ."

Abruptly, she stopped and stared at the strange woman. Her mouth opened again as if she were about to say something, then, as if that something had caught in her throat, she swallowed quickly and spat out a few words that hardly could be mistaken for a welcome, took a firm step backward, spun around, and stalked back through the entry that carried her into the compound of her own house.

"Come, children," their grandmother was saying as if she had not even noticed Olive's hurried arrival and immediate sulky departure. "Do you know who this beautiful creature is, this one who has come to grace our home with a visit today?"

Richard continued to stare at the woman. His throat, too, seemed to have developed sudden problems. And then the words pushed out. "Isn't that my mother?"

"Yes, my children. This is your dear mother, who has been gone from us for so long. Don't hesitate now to go to her and show your satisfaction that at last she has been able to come visit with us."

As if in a dream, Richard stepped one foot ahead of the other, right hand extended, his left resting politely on its inner forearm. His mouth automatically voiced the required greetings. Then, in the next instant, he found himself being gathered into his mother's arms with Shema and Marie-Pierre, being pressed against her heart. She bent over them, kissing each, murmuring to them, holding them close. Richard didn't want to move, didn't want to leave her side, but he heard his grandmother insisting that his mother come and sit and that she rest herself after such a long journey.

Reluctantly, he pulled back.

Just then, another voice split the afternoon.

16

The Hen Doesn't Crow

"Grandfather!" From under carefully lowered lids, Richard scrutinized the shuffling figure approaching the now-silent women. Shoes flapping around sockless feet, ancient gray suit jacket bagging from bony shoulders and hanging full around his dull plaid wraparound, limp brim of his favorite tan hat sagging widely over his ears, the man appeared to be nothing more than another ordinary old Rwandan wandering home from an uncharted itinerary on which his own unpredictable whims had taken him, yet Richard's hands slowly tightened into fists, and his body tensed.

If he . . . Toes digging a hold through the dust, Richard waited.

"Welcome . . . Come . . ."

Fragments of their exchange registered.

"In the shade . . ."

Richard's hands unfisted. His grandfather! Inviting his mother to sit! With him! In the shade of his favorite tree! He heard the old man order milk for "*our visitor.*" And sorghum wine. And then his own calabash of beer. Motioning Shema and Marie-Pierre to follow, Richard slipped around to an inconspicuous spot at the fringes of the shade and settled onto the ground. The adults acted as if this were a normal, any-day visit, picking up conversation as though they'd seen each other just the day before. And then another shadow fell.

Richard looked sideways.

His father stood in the entry.

Richard's breath caught.

His father hesitated.

Richard felt time lock into prolonged slowness.

His father crossed to the others. His mother stood. Their words echoed in some strange distance. His father lifted his hands and let them rest on his mother's shoulders. And then they sat. By the clay drinking pot. And his mother offered him the long reed straw through which she had been drinking. And . . .

Richard's breath sucked in quickly when he saw his father take the offered straw. And drink. *He still loves her! She can stay!*

The sun shone down from the heavenly blue, sliding around the comfortable shade under the spreading tree until it wrapped him in a warmth of happiness. *My father and my mother.* His thoughts soared. *Together.* Suddenly, his world was tied into a completeness he had never before known. Quiet fell over the four adults, and the only sounds other than the *sussing* as they nursed their drinking straws were those of some insects, a few birds, and an assortment of youngsters playing football in the distance. Ordinarily he would have slipped away and joined his buddies battling over the large brown banana-leaf ball, trying to kick it past the goalie and between the derelict bricks they'd built into temporary goal posts. But this was no ordinary day.

Then his grandfather spoke again. "Without feeling obliged to respond," he was saying, "tell me why you have opted for this way of living together without being together?"

Though his words said that for the moment he was not imposing his authority either as the eldest present or as family chief, everyone seemed to stiffen, and the old man himself was poised on his stool as if he were ready to bounce up and defend what had happened. After all, his order as family chief had expelled this woman from their midst, barring her from the husband who loved her, separating her from their tiny children, who by the law of traditions belonged to the father and were therefore confided to his mother, their paternal grandmother, for safekeeping and upbringing. Richard's insides turned topsy-turvy. Since the day his grandmother had told him about his mother, he'd often begged for more details.

"Your grandfather was impelled to send her away to save himself and to protect the entire family, including her," she had insisted time and again. "Hutu though he is, he cannot deny the part of Tutsi blood that he inherited through his own mother. Because of that, he always felt himself divided within his own skin. Independence may have brought us new freedoms, but it also created new dangers—the dangers of ethnic rivalry being expressed in a society that no longer had an outside force, the Belgian administration in our case, to hold the opposing sides in check. Like others of mixed heritage, he had to choose between the one tribe or the other. To prove himself worthy of the confidence of his Hutu neighbors and to protect the family from the carnage then being meted out against those who were not in Hutu favor, he chose to distance himself from everyone who was Tutsi and to show himself against everything he'd inherited from the Tutsi side. Some pure Tutsis even opted to support the Hutus. Others of mixed parentage sided with their Tutsi mothers, fleeing the country with the royalists, grouping with the Inyenzi, joining their attacks from the outside. Still others, Tutsis at heart, remained within the country, secretly collaborating with the Inyenzi, caching weapons, committing acts of treachery, doing everything possible to tear the power away from our new Hutu government and to reinstate the Tutsi monarchy. So you can understand that for the good of everyone, he had to make his position clear."

With all these antecedents and the tensions that now gripped the afternoon, Richard studied his mother's face, intent to know her response.

"We have always been reconciled to the measures in which our hearts have rested," she began, selecting her words in a way that would enable her to talk around the aim of the question. "And we have accepted this way of being blocked and unable to share in life as it may have been wished."

She continued speaking carefully, her tone soft, a slight smile tracing her lips. Though Richard applied all the understanding he had gained from his grandmother and endeavored to read meaning into each of her expressions and gestures, he could not understand anything other than that she neither attacked the old man nor did she entirely evade the issue. This was only normal, for Tutsis are skilled in maneuvering around an already-grave situation in order to avoid making it worse, and her speech revealed that she was a master at doing this. In addition, Tutsis know how to camouflage their true feelings.

Then it was his father's turn. After many long and polite excuses about the business matters that had kept him from being present when she'd arrived, Emmanuel's manner of address changed.

"Father."

Richard leaned forward as if to better understand.

"What inconvenience could it create now should Régine feel at home with her children here?"

The question hung, sharp with double-edged intention, and the man who was elder of this family shifted on his stool, his old face sagging with the effects of many difficult years. "My children," he said at last, and his features gathered into an almost smile. "If you only knew how the absence of this dear person has created such painful thoughts for me—I've had to sleep like a fish who can shut his eyes neither night nor day." With the skill that made him a favored orator for many of the community's festive occasions, he turned this lighthearted proverb toward the question. "Her return would not only help me to find my sleep again, but I also see that her children need the affection of their mother."

Had it been permitted, Richard at that point would have jumped up and cheered. Surely no mother could refuse such an offer. But he sat, as quiet as the shade itself, and waited while his grandmother refilled the pot of beer that the old man now, in a rare gesture, was sharing with his son. Then, at last, his mother spoke. After wandering through long and wordy phrases prescribed as proper expression of thanks to the family for the way in which she had been welcomed and the hospitality that had been extended to her person, she, in polite African manner, avoided brusque arrival at the point under discussion. "I would like to return to be with you," she finally said.

To hide the anticipation he felt, Richard picked up a twig and began tracing lines in the dust.

"But my mission today does not consist of anything more than coming so I could greet everyone, because, as you all know, this is a problem that needs to be discussed in its full context with all concerned. You know that I have my origins and that I'm not among those who are free to make such decisions. My wish is not very opposed to yours, but it would be better if all this could pass via the normal ways conceived by the predecessors in our culture."

Isn't she going to stay? Richard scraped a lopsided circle, then with a savage swipe cut an *x* across it. The twig snapped. *Doesn't she want to be with us?* He tossed the broken stick aside and in that moment noticed how the flowered cloth his mother wore knotted over her left shoulder contrasted prettily with her face. The cloth itself fell in soft folds over her long wraparound skirts. Pulling his knees tightly against his body with his arms, he let his eyes linger on her face. Often he'd closed his eyes and tried to imagine how she might look, and now, here she was, sitting in their very own yard, the features of her dark oval face smooth and serene. *Beautiful.* That's what she was. Even more beautiful than he'd ever dared to suppose. *Like a queen!* He swallowed with satisfaction. *My mother.*

"To cut myself short," she was saying, "I can say that I might anticipate coming back, but I don't find it without use to tell you of my concerns regarding cohabitation with your better one there—the one who gets angry without knowing the one with whom she is . . ."

"Régine!" Emmanuel lashed her name out.

She closed her lips as though she had finished her sentence. "There are certain affairs!"

Richard's hands unconsciously fisted, and a shiver twitched along his back. Then when his father actually pronounced Olive's name, he felt the heat begin to rise along his neck.

"Never! Never!" Emmanuel's mouth opened wider and wider. "There are limits to which you will submit yourself in regard to . . ." The shade resting lightly over her shoulders, Régine placidly regarded Emmanuel, a faint smile tracing her lips, as he passionately defended Olive.

"Olive?" Suddenly the elder of the two women bobbed forward and pounded a string of words toward her youngest begotten, like the punches of a boxer, letting them fall hard and direct. "What are you saying? What sense have these words? That woman has no pride. No likeness to our Régine. Have you forgotten who is the mother of . . ."

"Enough!" His grandfather's arms swung windmill-like in the direction of his wife. "Such impropriety! Do you hear? Zis ish henough!"

"What has Régine done?" The old woman swung her words toward both men. "Certainly nothing to deserve this!"

"In-ap-pro-pri-ate."

"Never!" Emmanuel was shouting.

"Régine deserves . . ."

"Zhuh feminine gender shpeaking in zhuh presence huf men!" Despite the inebriated slurring of his tongue, his grandfather struggled to order this female underling of his into line. Richard glanced sideways at his two little sisters, perched on the ground like two little rock carvings with eyes huge enough and round enough to bring them both toppling forward. "Zhuh hen doeshn't crow if zhuh rooshter iz dere!"

"The hen!" At that, the old woman bounced up as though knocked to her feet by the insult of her husband's proverb. She jumped in front of Régine and let out a piercing scream. It tore from her throat, pitching up and up, shrilling into a long *eeeeeeeeee* dipping and lifting again and again.

Régine sat, unmoving, a picture of complete composure.

The men fell silent.

Abruptly, the old woman stopped and sat down. With her cry, the Rwandan variation of the trilling ululation used through the centuries by African women to express joy and appreciation, she had made her point.

When conversation finally resumed again, the nuances strayed carefully beyond the fringes of the subject that had brought them into sharp dispute and at the same time also took it beyond the capacity of Richard's comprehension. He knew that decisions were being made. But what were they? The afternoon dragged on. The grown-ups fell more and more under the spell of their drink.

He began to sigh.

No one seemed to notice.

His sighs became louder.

Still the adults ignored him. A child was not to make himself heard in the presence of his elders, not until he was at least eighteen, and then only after having proved his manhood at a special drinking feast.

In Rwanda, drinking and life go together. Beer is considered a necessity at all social occasions, formal and informal. Banana plantations prodigiously cover the country, and almost every traditional family holding has its pit for curing bananas, as well as a hollowed-out log trough for working them into juice and a quantity of brewing pots. Banana beer, sorghum beer, wine, whiskey, and other beverages are never lacking, for one must always provide a drink—if not milk, at least something alcoholic—to share with one's guests. Those whose Christian churches have convinced them to abstain from alcohol never fail to offer fresh banana juice or soft drinks, though such is considered a waste by the majority who hold to the traditions. In any case, refusing an offered drink is a serious insult, and drunkenness holds no shame, since it marks the prosperous man. Therefore, at his coming-of-age feast, a young man is expected to show his capacity to hold his drink.

On the day of the feast, a large gray clay drinking pot, at least knee-high and very wide, will be filled with a strong alcoholic drink until a tan froth bubbles above its opening. The boy and his father seat themselves by the pot, each at one of the eight or twelve long, jointed reed straws placed in it, and to prove himself, the boy must drink until his father has had enough and then continue drinking without falling into a drunken stupor. In traditional society, never, except by permission of an elder, will a young man be able to speak in the presence of adults until he has passed this test.

Richard sighed again. Several times. Each time louder and louder. "What is it, my child?" his mother finally asked.

That was all the permission he needed. "My mother's coming has made this the happiest day of my life, and her presence with us would be . . ." His words rushed out before one of the others could interrupt. Then he came to the one thing that lay heaviest on his young heart, a problem for which he now implored his mother's intervention—the treatment he, Shema, and Marie-Pierre were forced to endure at the hands of the one about whom they'd had such a lively dispute, Olive, their father's second wife.

CHAPTER 17

A Queen Among Queens

The sun, a muted orange-red disk, had nearly touched the top of the distant hills. "Be courageous." Régine slipped her arms around Richard when they reached the edge of his grandfather's property, the place of proper leave-taking when anyone came to visit, and she pulled his thin body close to hers. "Remember." Her whisper brushed his ear. "We are staying together." She turned to include Shema and Marie-Pierre in her embrace, then pointed them back toward the house. "Take good care of your little sisters." Régine laid her hand on her eldest child's shoulder, squeezing it softly, and the boy tilted up his face. As his deep brown eyes met hers, he was thinking of all the many times he had saved secrets away, guarding them inside himself until she would come and he would have the opportunity to share them with the woman who was his mother. "I . . ." His childish treble trailed away. None of what he had earlier wanted to talk about seemed important now. "I will," he finally said, then with hesitant lips added, "Mother."

"And I'll return shortly." She bent, brushing his cheek with her lips, then straightened, and with long skirts swishing softly against her ankles, walked with purposeful steps into the golden path spread by the setting sun.

An intense burning spread down his throat and into his chest. "Mother!" he wanted to shout after the graceful silhouette retreating so rapidly and leaving him so completely behind. "Don't go!" He wanted to run after her, to grab her arm, to stop her, but his feet clamped him firmly, as though they were rooted to the hard, dusty path. He flipped his arm, making his fingers snap. *It's not fair! Grandfather! Why?* Again he flipped his arm, and his thumb slid against his fingers with an angry snap that filled the void left by his unspoken disappointment. When the old man had called for the *agashinguracumu*—his way as host of saying that the next beer to be brought would be the last for the day and that when it was gone, guests would be expected to take their leave—he had willed everyone to drink slowly. Very slowly. But all too soon the calabash had stood empty. Yet his mother hesitated.

"You will be staying?" Of course, the others had to say that. Even Richard understood that. Not a one of them expected her to stay. Except ... *Stay,* he had begged deep inside his heart. But he knew, even at his age, that if she did pass the night within the walls of the enclosure that included his father's house and then was seen leaving the next day to go back to her own family, the neighbors would be quick with words about the kind of person she was. Now with chest burning and eyes dry and scratchy, he watched her follow the road and disappear behind the long, white-trunked row of eucalyptus trees. His shoulders sagged. He let his head drop forward to hide the fact that his eyes were no longer dry, and a rude tingling settled over the back of his neck. His throat ached. From somewhere near the house, he heard Shema and Marie-Pierre laugh as if they did not have the sense to realize that their mother had gone. That she had been forced to leave them behind. Again.

"Return?" He shook his drooping head. Adults were always full of promises, and then, later, always just as full of excuses as to why those promises were taking so long to find their way into reality. He kicked at a dry clod, catching it with his toes and curling it up and over the grasses edging the path, and then heard it land with a hollow *thunk*. He also heard the distant bleat of a goat, the mooing of some cattle, a dog barking, people talking. A breeze stirred through the bananas, setting the leaves to a soft *thwacking*. The light was fading, and he forced himself to turn and go. By the time he slipped on silent feet through the back entrance, dusk had settled into full darkness, and Malachai already had the evening fire burning. He traced his way around the edges of its light.

"The colonishts. They're the onesh resphonshible."

Richard stopped short. His grandfather, his stool in its usual place near the house door, slouched with head down, his flute dangling loosely in his thickly veined, bony hands, and he appeared to be talking to the ground.

"Having to chase people away. No one worried before zhen 'bout eshnic. Nobody cared about Hutush-Tutshi."

Richard listened. The old man's slurred excuses tumbled downward, as if he were unloading responsibility from his conscience and transferring it to those who were no longer there. *Mama!* The word flashed through his mind, and with a start, he understood. *That's who he's talking about! Mama!*

"Shertainly Hutush needed to claim shertain rights. Shertainly Hutush had been under a heavy yoke of vasshal and mashter. Shertainly they wanted cowsh." At that point, the old man straightened, and his jowl sagged uncomprehendingly while he swung his head slowly from side to side as though searching for someone. Then he saw Richard. "The cowsh!" he exclaimed with sudden vigor. "Hash Malachai shtarted milking the cowsh?"

"I'll go see." Before any inactivity on his part could be magnified into something reprehensible by his grandfather's inebriated condition, Richard's legs quickly carried him in the direction of the cows. And just as quickly, he found himself plowing into a bristly wall of something.

"Richard!" Shema's indignant squeal caught him off guard. "Watch where you're going!" He shoved out, and the load of grass toppled from her head. "Richard!" she squealed again, but he ignored her and kicked at the dull hump intended as a part of the fresh bedding for his grandfather's herds and scattered it. "See!" He kicked again. "I'm helping you. Doing girl's work!"

At any other time, Shema would have found some scathing return for the way he had knocked the grass where she didn't want it, for the way he curled the word *girl,* but she ignored her brother's peevishness. "Malachai's waiting for you." Her words were more of a warning. "And Grandmother says you had better hurry 'cause she doesn't want anyone to upset Grandfather tonight. He's very drunk, you know!"

"I know."

"Don't you think our mama is pretty?"

Richard started to open his mouth to say Yes, but just as suddenly he shut it. The suddenness of Shema's question made that hot prickliness come back into his throat.

"When do you think she'll come back?"

"I . . ." He stared down and seemed to notice that the grass needed to be rearranged with his foot. "Dunno," he mumbled. "Malachai's waiting."

"Intashyo." Their Hutu servant directed the word toward Richard as though it were an order as he nodded toward a large, bony shape standing apart from the others. Richard went to the cow—the top of his head barely reached her shoulder—and pushed his body against her side. He felt her supple hide quiver, gathering into a quick series of ripples intended to shake away this intruder in the same way she chased flies. Her long tail arched around, slapping its brushy tip against Richard's arm.

"Intashyo," he whispered.

She flicked her ear then, as if surprised and pleased to hear her name, and the quivering stopped.

"How beautiful you are." He looped his arms over her back, scratching his fingers along her spine, and the warmth of her ample flank felt good against his skin, and it soaked cozily through the thinness of his shirt. The cow relaxed now and seemed to be pleased by his touch, and with the words he spoke, "a queen among queens." He heard the splat of milk against the bottom of the wooden milk pot Malachai held. "Such lovely eyes, brown and understanding. Gentle. Kind." He let his head drop forward, and he nuzzled it against her shoulder. "You will care for us. Generously and tenderly, you will see to all our needs. And protect us." His whispers, directed toward the ears of this long-horned matriarch of the herd, began to flow with the same rhythms his grandfather used in his poetry, which everyone liked so much, and like his grandfather's, his words, though spoken to and about a cow, were intended to describe a person. "Beautiful!" he repeated. "A queen among queens." And he was thinking not of Intashyo but instead of his mother.

"We aren't in any condition to receive any *good evenings!*"

At sounds of the screamed outburst pouring through the hedge, his head lifted suddenly, and his hand involuntarily clamped against Intashyo's neck.

"That's for your other one! The beautiful one!"

"Olive!" His father's voice rang out sharply. Then it pitched down so Richard could no longer understand the words, but that quiet did not last.

"All afternoon!" Olive screeched. "With her as though . . ."

At that moment, his grandmother came to take the full milk pot from Malachai and give him another. He could see the glow of the fire reflecting in her eyes. "Such a difference," she murmured.

With a feeling of quick pride, Richard nodded to show that he understood. His mother would never shout like that. Hadn't he seen that for himself that very afternoon? His mother was Tutsi, and Tutsis knew how to hide their anger.

"I love her." Emmanuel's voice raised defiantly.

"Love . . . !" Olive's shriek curled into a prime exhibit that Hutu anger, once aroused, was unmistakable and obvious.

"I have always loved her." Richard's hands muscled into Intashyo's shoulder as he heard his father. "No matter what you do, you can never stop her from returning!"

That night, Richard did not sleep.

"I will return." Whispers of the gentle voice twined and retwined with echoes of his father's shouted threat. "You can't stop her." The next morning, just as Richard was leaving for school with Shema and Marie-Pierre, Olive barred their way.

"Bring me water!" she snapped. "Before you go to school."

Marie-Pierre turned wide eyes toward her brother. "But teacher . . ."

She had no chance to finish her sentence, because their father's voice shouted from the other side of the hedge. "Send your own children to get your water!"

Olive swiveled.

The three children stared.

Like an enraged chicken, mouth wide open, angry squawks pumping out and wings beating the air, Olive stamped back into her own yard. The three children turned and fled like startled antelope down the path toward school.

"Her children!" Richard exclaimed when they were safely beyond earshot. "Papa said that!"

Olive had been their father's wife for more than four years, and still she had no children. "A woman who can't bear children!" As well as being hard-working and modest, a woman was a taken-for-granted vessel of fertility. Since nothing is more agreeable to the heart than to reproduce oneself in children, as their proverb says, no self-respecting Rwandan male would think of marrying for simple cohabitation or merely for love, and a woman's esteem raises in proportion to the number of children she bears. Olive was, in the eyes of everyone, herself the one responsible for this disadvantaged childless state. The ancestors never could accept a man as being the one at fault. In any case, Rwandan families know how to test the woman in question with a brother of the husband, and Richard and his sisters were all the proof their father needed.

"What good is a woman like that?" The neighbors' comments about Olive gave Richard more than necessary satisfaction. "The good-for-nothing!" Plumping his hands against his sides, he mimicked sarcastic neighborhood voices.

"Embarrassing," their grandmother grumbled when the children arrived home after school. "All morning. Shouting. Insulting your father and your mother. Your grandfather. And even my very own person. That woman has no shame! Carrying on like that in full view of everyone!" Well-bred Rwandans of both tribes never allow family problems to escape the intimacy of the family, preferring to keep their disputes until after darkness has fallen and then conducting them only inside the confines of their homes, hedged in for the very reason of allowing them to live discreetly and to maintain their privacy. "She's lost her dignity as a woman!"

The old woman stood, one hand on a hip and the other pressed against the breast of her faded T-shirt as she regarded the three children who were still her trust. A chicken picked in the dust near her bare feet. To the side, one of her Muscovy ducks slopped in a pan of leftover dishwater. "My daughters." She addressed herself to Shema and Marie-Pierre. "No matter what she might say or do, never dishonor my teaching by allowing her despicable behavior to incite you to do anything similar or of such a disgraceful nature. Always remember the art of silence. Remember that reticence and gentleness are the marks to be respected in a woman."

The girls, of course, promised.

18

The First Earth

A collection of uncles, heads of various branches of the extended family, and older cousins circled the calabash while the evening firelight played drab designs across their fatigued shirts and tossed strange, elongated shadows on the ground behind them. "If the government . . ." Dark spaces gapped around the elder uncle's two gray-yellow top teeth. Caught by the fire's light, the two bobbed up and down like misshapen fangs while he threaded politics with cows and crops in a wandering, high-pitched nasal commentary. His voice whined into a thin thread, spiraling into the distance, and the bobbing teeth faded while Richard pondered his own problems. *When Mama comes back . . .* He crossed his legs, pulling his knees against his chest, picked up a twig with two lifeless brown leaves, and spun it between his fingers. The leaves fanned out like the propellers on the imaginary airplanes he and his playmates made from sorghum leaves and sticks. *Maybe then . . .* She had visited twice since that first Sunday, and after her last visit, his father had suddenly become interested in putting walls on the foundation that had lain forgotten for so many years near the commercial center.

"They had expected to live there." His grandmother's commentary explained how his parents had planned to build a big, beautiful house with many rooms and windows and a metal roof. "But until now, he never touched it after she left."

The leaf propeller twirled a breath of air across his cheek, but he dropped it and let his arms drape around his knees, elbows drooping downward. The wavering firelight. The men's voices. The insects. His head begin to sag forward. Every morning before sunup, his grandfather called him from bed, made him work, made him fill his days with a monotonously exhausting drama of tending the cows, helping Malachai, carrying water, fetching firewood, going to school, doing more chores. He had complained about his grandfather's hardness to himself, to his grandmother, to his sisters, and to Frank. "If he weren't here, I could run this place with my eyes closed," he had grumbled to Frank just that afternoon. He had wanted to stay after school and play football, but his grandmother needed more firewood, and he had orders to take the long detour home and gather dry branches at the edge of the forest. "I wish he liked me better. Then he would let me play. When my mama comes . . ."

Head lolling against his knees, he stared past the men, past the wavering light, and into the shadowy darkness. He was aware that the others had fallen silent and that his grandfather's voice again dominated the interminable debates that the men picked up and rehashed every time they got together. ". . . and therefore I must do all in my power so that in case of my death there will be . . ."

The words bore into Richard's consciousness.

". . . a man to whom will pass everything of mine on the day I die."

"Die?" Richard straightened.

"I do not wish to leave behind me some irresponsible dog who has no sense about what he should do. I have tried in every way possible to maintain the dignity of the family, and I have always wished that the one who will assume my existence after I die will also be a man with a capital *M*."

Richard stared toward his grandfather. "Why this talk about dying?" The old man was tough. Tough almost to the point of being a tyrant. But life without him?

"For the reason that this be taken as a testament in my memory, let it be known that the one to take over after my death is this young fellow here." Everyone turned, and Richard felt the dozen and some pairs of eyes fix on him. "He is to be the one who will serve me with the first earth."

"The first earth?" Suddenly, Richard's thoughts were racing. "Such is the secret revealed that needs to be remembered. Take it seriously, and respect it to the letter as my testament made before witnesses." In traditional law, what had just been said in the presence of the family elders was as binding as any written legal document. Richard was to be his grandfather's heir. The next morning, he was awake before sunrise, before his grandfather came to call, and he hurried out to have everything ready when Malachai came to milk. *If grandfather weren't here, I could run this place. I could!*

His grandfather pulling him from bed before dawn, making him do too many chores, making him responsible for the cows, making him learn. He could herd and milk; he could even draw a cow's blood, just as his ancestors had. That was easy, the way his grandfather had taught him to do it, a simple matter of going over to a cow while it grazed, talking to it, rubbing its back, then with a quick jab piercing a lance into its flank and letting the blood flow into a collecting pot. If you did it right, a cow hardly noticed, and afterward all you had to do was pinch the hide together. Many times he had done it and had taken the blood to the house for his grandmother to cook it, as their ancestors had, into that sort of paste everyone liked so well. Yes, he could already do all that and more because . . . *Grandfather's been training me?*

Intashyo was already on her feet and at the sound of the boy's voice turned her head in his direction, her long, blunted, ivory-gray horns crooked upward, her large brown eyes soft and motherly. He went to her and slipped his arms around her neck. "Intashyo," he whispered, nuzzling his head against the coarse hide. He felt the shift of her body as she pushed herself closer against him. "Intashyo," he whispered again. "Grandfather loves me. He makes me work because he loves me."

The months passed.

Emmanuel finished the house near the commercial center.

Régine returned.

Richard and Shema and Marie-Pierre moved with her into the new house.

"Mother." Two candles burned on their stands, casting cheery profiles of four newly purchased upholstered chairs onto the freshly painted wall. "We . . ." Richard felt the next words squeeze in his throat. "That is to say . . ." He cleared his throat, hoping that would help to steady his voice. "We are very happy you have returned to be with us. For a long time, we have looked forward to this day." His gaze framed his mother, and the long speech he had planned in honor of her return suddenly became lost in his smile, and the smile that he smiled was not one of those smiles he had been taught to use to show politeness or to hide his true feelings from others. It came from the very center of his being. "Our life is now complete."

Some days Emmanuel was with them; some days he stayed with Olive at his other house. That also became a piece of the pattern their new life assumed. And then his grandfather took sick. Richard trudged across town and along the road on his way to visit the old man. A breeze stirred, flipping around the long, flat, vibrant green leaves of the banana plants on one side of the road, scattering a soft clacking across the close-planted field as the solid foliage flapped together. On the other side, two younger cousins matched skills with their homemade tops.

"Where are the calves?"

At his hollered question, the boys waved toward a lower corner of the field, but Richard did not stop to talk. Instead, he turned onto the path that led through the bananas. When he entered the house and saw his grandfather, the sunken face and the thin outline of the wasted body under the gray blanket, he wanted to turn his head, to leave. Instead, he dutifully took a stool near the bedside. The old man roused, saw that Richard had come, and asked about his school, then about whether Malachai had finished cultivating the lower field.

"He still has the men working there and says that perhaps they will have it ready so that they can begin planting sorghum tomorrow."

Richard's reply seemed to satisfy the old man, and he lapsed again into the hazy world inhabited by the elderly when their strength has been drained by a long illness.

Say something more, Grandfather. Richard willed the silent figure to understand his unspoken wish. *Please say something to me and tell me that you were not happy about that time I was condemned to live without my mother; say that you regret the part you were forced to play in sending her away. Grandfather, please. Don't leave me like this. Don't. Let me know you're sorry.* But he put nothing of those thoughts into real words.

The old man roused from time to time, sometimes speaking unintelligible things belonging to a time unknown to Richard, sometimes aware and interested in those who had come to wait with him, sometimes asking about the cows and where Malachai had taken them that day, but never touching the one thing that Richard hoped against hope to hear.

And then toward evening of another day, his grandfather slipped away from the land of the living. "The will of Imana," murmured the adults. And sadly everyone accepted the old man's departure as another fateful slice in the grand scheme determining human destiny, knowing that they, too, would ultimately be forced to join him in order to play out the fates as determined by their distant and unapproachable deity.

The next afternoon, Richard let himself be pushed through the close-standing crowd, following the opening that parted zipperlike just long enough for him to pass and then closed again behind him. Gregoire, the husband of his father's eldest sister, thrust the hoe-shaped branch into his hands. It felt stiff and awkward, but holding it as he had been shown, he numbly went from corner to corner of the open grave to throw down the three scoops of earth from each, as he had been told that he must do. His head hardly reaching to the chests of the men around him, his slight form rigid, Richard lifted the last scoop of earth and let it fall downward onto the silent, shrouded body while the chanting voice of one of the elders repeated the prescribed litany. Their beliefs taught that a person who has had children never disappears, and the words spoken now were intended to link his departed grandfather to the living through the heir he had designated to represent him. Small though he was even for his twelve years, Richard stood as that new family chief, the representative his grandfather had left on earth. The respect that had belonged to the old man was now his. His grandmother would from that day onward address him as "my husband," and he would care for her needs as a husband, though not in the matters of conjugal life. Even his father in certain circumstances would be expected to submit to his word.

If someone hurt him, it would be an indirect attack on the old man, and the anger of the old man's spirit might fall upon the one responsible. The old ones who remained, especially those who awaited their own soon departure to the spirit world deep within the craters of the great volcanoes to the west, would of necessity show respect to Richard, hoping in that way to appease and mollify the capricious whims of the one who had gone before and therefore ease their own entry when the time came for them to join him. With the ceremony of the first earth having been completed, the boy looked around, hoping to spot the parish curé, wanting him to say a word on his grandfather's behalf.

"Wouldn't come to this one," someone muttered behind him. "The old one didn't bother much with the church and made no secret about his belief in the ancestors."

Many, even among the Christians, still followed cultural rites, arguing that the saints have no more value than their ancestors, and in the huts devoted to calming the departed spirits, they made offerings to appease envious grandfathers and others who they believed would jealously send misfortune, sickness, crop failure, and cattle epidemics on those enjoying cherished possessions that they had been forced to leave behind. The unmarried, the young departed who in life had not yet gained the maturity to repress their anger, needed the extra precaution of being buried with a piece of charcoal in their spear hand, symbolic of the fire that cleanses away evil. That would prevent their ghosts from coming back maliciously to perturb those who remained.

The crowd fell back again, and a young brown heifer was led toward Richard. *Beautiful*, he thought, admiring her solid, promising form. But as she was presented to him, symbol of all he had inherited, the women stood silent. They dared not break into their shrill ululations, the high-pitched cries of joy that belong with the presentation of a gift of herds. His grandfather was gone.

The ceremonies of mourning lasted for one week after the interment. During that time, the family was strictly forbidden to eat meat of any kind—the spirits would have looked upon such imprudence as being the same as eating the one who had died. Then on the evening when they could again return to their own house, Richard led the way. Everything that had been his grandfather's did belong to him, but nearly everything, including the heifer that had been given him at the burial, remained with his grandmother. Olive still lived across from her in his father's house. Even now his father was there. With her. Richard trudged along the beaten path that led away from the old home and toward the commercial center. In his hands he carried his grandfather's spear, his flute, and his baton, the staff of office that was now his as chief of the family. Given the unpredictability of the spirits, no one in the clan would think of touching those items without Richard's express permission.

19

Caught

A year later, Richard stood midcampus, his neat white shirt and crisp khaki shorts marking him as one of the boys. Hills rolled away from the beautiful buildings, away from the tall mango trees and the healthy green rice fields, away from the fine gardens and nearby lake and toward the distant mountains. From among all who had asked, he was one of the few who had been chosen. He had been given the privilege of coming to this beautiful spot in their beautiful country. He was among those who were to become sowers of the Word of the Creator. Already he had adapted to the calm, to the ceremonial ritual of prayer, to the list of rules that all were required to follow in strict obedience. When vacation time came, he accepted as his due the admiring glances everyone gave his neat uniform and the matching white bag he carried on his shoulder, and he gloried in the joy of his grandmother and his mother, who happily praised him for being among those who one day could join the ranks of the priests of their church.

"A simple priest! Not this one!" His grandmother's bragging words to Régine were meant for Richard's ears. "This one of ours has a future. One day he will be *Monseigneur!*"

Richard smiled with satisfaction then. No Rwandan young man was expected to content himself with being a common anything. Service jobs in general were looked down upon, especially in the early years after independence. If a school graduate did not make it into a government or civil service position, he was expected to aim for the highest position that belonged to his calling. Power was almost everything. "Never mistreat a child," a new proverb warned. "Someday he may be president."

I will be somebody, he promised himself. *For the sake of my mother and my grandmother, I will be somebody.* And as if the act itself would seal that promise, he joined with a small group of boys who maintained a prayer vigil every evening after their study hour. "If You will help me in my studies, I will devote my life to the church," he repeated again and again. Before the school year ended, though, he was called home to bury his grandmother.

"I'll remember," he whispered, hoping that somehow her spirit would hear and that she would know he would do his best to fulfill her wishes regarding his future. "I'll always respect everyone as you have taught me, and I will use my capabilities and my gifts to serve with the chosen of God. You'll see. I'll study hard. I'll do well, and one day I will be the Monseigneur, the leader of our church in Rwanda. I will do everything in my power so that you will be considered as one of the great educators of our people."

On a clear and sunny afternoon during the next school year, while waiting with his class for their group swimming lesson at the lake, he flopped himself down onto the beach. Glancing around, he saw none of the teachers. Quickly, he flipped over onto his stomach and let the warmth of the sand soak into his body.

"Richard!"

Startled, he scrambled to his feet. A rotund figure glared at him. "Come here!"

Richard obeyed. Automatically. But the closer his steps carried him, the bigger and more fearsome the man appeared. The large brown eyes. The big, bristly mustache. The off-white cassock bunching around the thick belly and hanging down to almost touch the heavy black shoes. The nearer he got, the more unwieldy his own feet felt, and he braced himself, mentally sure that as soon as he was within range, one of those big heavy shoes would be lashed out to catch him like a club. He'd seen other boys doubled in silent pain from their big chief's methods of discipline.

"Kneel!"

Richard dropped, hands clasped, still braced for a blow. But the big European turned and with robes swishing strode off. Richard held himself immobile in the position of penance, hoping against hope that the man's anger would be spent by the time he returned. Surely, with this being his first offense ever—he'd only been lying on his stomach, nothing else—this punishment would be adequate. Then he heard the heavy steps retracing their way back toward the spot where he knelt. He kept his eyes submissively lowered.

"Get up!"

Richard pushed himself to his feet.

"Go to my office. We'll see there what is to be done with you! Such behavior! So divergent from the straight path of the elected! You deserve to be expelled!"

Richard trudged ahead of the man in dutiful silence. *Be expelled?* His misdemeanor, he knew, in no way merited such an extreme punishment. Then, almost before he realized what was happening, he was being sent on to the rector's office.

"For this you will be suspended for three weeks, at the end of which time you will return to our school with your father."

Stunned, Richard collected his things, packed his white seminary bag, and headed toward the road for this out-of-season journey to his home.

"Look! The little *umuzungu* [White man] has returned!"

Jealous neighbors—especially since his mother's return, when they had moved into the big new house above the market—ridiculed the family for trying to live like the Whites.

"Thought he was going to be a priest!"

In Rwanda, as in much of Africa, individuals rarely find joy in a neighbor's successes. If someone does well, others become jealous. Rather than try to better their own way of living, they search for ways to bring him down. To make him fall from his privileged status. This is particularly true in regard to those who succeed in school.

"A consequence of his disturbed childhood," Richard heard his mother confiding to a friend, one whom she could trust. "Because of my long absence."

"No, Mama," he argued later. "Not because of you. This problem is only because of the school."

The three weeks finally dragged to an end, and Emmanuel drove him back to the campus in the old Peugeot he'd recently been able to buy. Since Régine's return, business was improving for him, both in his wholesale marketing and in the new bar he'd built. At the seminary gate, a priest greeted them with a reassuring smile and showed them to the proper office. "Are you the father of this unsuccessful padre?" the rector asked, smiling.

"Yes, but I'm confident that with your assistance he won't disappoint us again."

The prefect nodded. "In making important decisions, though, we also need the parents' participation."

"When we bring you our children and leave them in your hands, that's a sign of our confidence in you," Emmanuel responded. "I don't see anything inconvenient in punishing the child in this situation. Neither do I see the necessity of my presence, except if there is something . . ."

"We don't disagree with you in respect to that," interrupted the rector. "By the way, has Richard told you the reason for which he was inflicted with this punishment and asked to leave our establishment?"

"That's only normal," replied Emmanuel. "And even if he had endeavored to hide the reason, it's among my responsibilities as his father to ask him and to know why this has happened. That is especially true since I also am the one who must acquit myself of my responsibilities regarding the school fees."

"A-huumm, ye-es," the rector agreed, "that is the way it should be. And, Richard, would you do us the kindness of repeating your fault before us just as you presented it to your family?"

"When I arrived at the house, I told them that I was sent home for three weeks because I had lain on my stomach at the beach and I was caught by the prefect."

"Don't you know that's a fault for which the punishment is automatic? Don't you know that it is on the list of specifically banned behaviors in our code of conduct?"

"Yes, I know."

"Then why did you do it?"

"I . . . I . . . I . . ."

Turning toward Emmanuel and before Richard could collect his thoughts and present a logical explanation, the rector said, "See, my brother in Christ, you yourself can make your own judgment as to the propriety of his behavior. But as for us, we find, after long and deliberate reflection, that it is inadmissible to keep libertines in the midst of our sacred family. Thus we ask that you will accommodate our decision by taking this young man with you. When you yourself have become assured that he has again taken up the way of the good sheep and is willing to fit himself into our community, perhaps then he can be returned to us."

Richard heard his father's breath draw in sharply. "But isn't there some way for you yourselves to help him in the correction of his behavior? Would it not be better that he stay here to continue studying with his colleagues?"

"For me the curtain has been drawn." Again the rector's smile slipped into place on his beatified face. "And so as not to detain you unnecessarily, the prefect will help you with all the necessary arrangements. With that being the case, we will await your next visit."

At the dormitory, Richard collected his belongings from his room, and together he and Emmanuel packed them into the old Peugeot.

"What's happening?" A boy coming in from class looked from the box Richard carried to the old car parked by the road; then he glanced hurriedly in every direction. "Are you leaving?" He spoke in whispers now.

Richard nodded.

More boys gathered. "Leaving? Why?" Whispers scattered through the group. "Because of what happened at the beach?" Several heads shook in amazement.

"Watch out! Someone's coming!"

The hissed warning sent the boys scattering to their rooms.

"Not allowed to speak to strangers," Richard mumbled to Emmanuel. "Not without permission."

"But you're . . ."

"No longer a student." Richard pushed past his father and shoved the last box into the back seat.

"Animals!" Emmanuel gripped the steering wheel and aimed the old car through the gate and toward the road. "I didn't think these holy men of God would react like such animals!" He gritted his teeth. "A mere boy. One mistake. And like that. Out. Ah, my child." He now spoke directly to Richard. "Even if that's what you want, don't go back to them. Don't. Not ever! Imana has another plan for you."

"It is the plan of God!" his mother agreed, covering her disappointment at having her son back home so immediately and so permanently. "My child, perhaps you will now be able to succeed in something else. Or maybe, one day . . ." She brightened and smiled. "Maybe they'll call you to come back. The goodness of your heart can change your destiny."

Hearing that proverb was just the encouragement Richard needed. Day after day passed. Night after night he ritually repeated, "And if I am taken back, I will devote my life to prayer." And he waited, looking for the letter that would say he was being invited to return to the school.

"What do they want with worthless dogs? They'll never have you back."

Following his mother's advice, Richard ignored Olive's gloating taunts until the day, not many weeks later, when the parish curé (priest) arrived to see Emmanuel. In private. "The authorities at the Petit Seminaire have asked that I come to inform you regarding Richard's situation," he began.

"Oh, I see, and I'm glad to hear they are thinking about the boy." Emmanuel saw with satisfaction that his visitor was enjoying the beer that had been brought for him. "And do our worthy authorities at the institution recognize the injustice that has been committed before God by sending this child away from their halls of learning?"

"Well, aahhh, ah-hummmh." The curé carefully cleared his throat.

"That is to say that, as they have explained it to me, it seems that the boy has as root cause to his problem at least two reasons."

"Two reasons." Emmanuel nodded his head reflectively.

"Two reasons," the priest repeated and twisted as if searching for a position that would better lend itself to explanation of the double argument that had brought him. Then he repeated everything he had said before, adding even more words this second time, which contributed nothing of information regarding the actual message. Finally, he said, "The first of these reasons involves the undisciplined conduct that you are no doubt aware the boy committed at the Petit Seminaire, and for which conduct he has been duly punished. That is the first reason."

Emmanuel made no move to add any commentary.

"The second reason, and—uh—aahhh—aahhh-humghm . . ." The priest started to cough and then proceeded to clear his throat even more vigorously. "That is to say . . ." His voice blurted out quite clearly now. "That is to say that the second reason is perhaps an even greater reason." And again he repeated himself at length, circling back to emphasize that the nature of Richard's original misconduct concerned a bodily misdeed that could not be countenanced within the context of such a sacred setting. "This being an even greater problem in view of the fact it has been determined that there is a certain problem within the family."

Emmanuel waited for the priest to explain himself. It was common knowledge to all adherents of the church during that era that the religious practices of the family were carefully scrutinized in order to establish the purity of their religious profession before any boy would be considered as a candidate into the seminary, and Emmanuel's arrangement with the former priest had ensured that he would recommend Richard as coming from an upright and respected family of the church.

"That is to say," the curé began again before adding, "that the fact of polygamy has been discovered in this family."

"Polygamy." Emmanuel repeated the word as though he'd been betrayed. Though polygamy is traditionally an established practice in Rwanda, the strong Catholic influence in the country had made the custom of having more than one wife against both state law and the church.

Children coming from families with polygamous arrangements were not to be admitted into the seminary. Emmanuel's money had in its own way convinced the previous curé not to consider Olive as a second wife.

"The man who cannot lie cannot feed his family," Emmanuel had quipped to Régine, pleased when he could bring her the good news that the way had been cleared for Richard to sit for the examination.

She, as usual, had said nothing that her husband could later turn against her.

"Since we have learned that the other woman is indeed living with you as a second wife," the curé now continued, "Richard is expelled for good. He is not to return."

20

Haricot

"See! What did I tell you!"

Richard hunched against the back wall of their house, scrunching small as he used to do when he wanted to stay out of Olive's sight. Only he wasn't small anymore, and he no longer had to hide from her rude orders. Even so, echoes of the harsh taunts he had heard her throw at his father the afternoon before throbbed in his ears.

"A no-good dog!"

He dropped his head against his knees. He knew what she meant. Everyone knew what she meant. He had been expelled from the seminary. *Expelled! For good!* By law, that meant the end of his schooling. "Because . . ." His hands clenched and unclenched. "Because of *her!*"

"Not to worry, my son. You'll not have to stay like this forever." When Richard tried to talk to his father about Olive, Emmanuel, as usual, had evasively circumvented Richard's complaints. "No matter what has been done by those at the seminary who consider themselves so pious, they're not going to be able to be destroy your life."

"But, Papa, she won't stop with just words." Richard intended to make his point. "She . . ."

"Patience, my son. Your aunt there . . ."

Richard's insides revolted every time his father referred to Olive as "your aunt there." "She's not my aunt!" he had wanted to yell, but he dared not show such disrespect to his own father.

"You must understand and remember that while she may have her certain backgrounds and her own fashion of expressing herself at the time, she would never do a thing to hurt your person. You are my son. You are never to guard such thoughts in your head. I have said this to you many times before, and now I ask . . ."

"But, Papa, she . . ." In their own language with its richness in nuances and double meanings, the same term is used for both polygamy and jealousy.

"No!" Emmanuel had remained firm. "You are not to speak against her in that fashion. Not again." Then he abruptly changed his manner of approach. "My son, this will pass. You are not going to have to stay like this, because we're going to find you another school."

"But, Papa, I . . ."

Richard wished he could tell his father that he wanted the way to be unblocked so that he could go back to the seminary. But he knew, even against all the hopes he had built inside himself, that even if Emmanuel would take measures to repudiate his second wife, it would be too late. They had made up their minds. They would never have him back. He could never become a priest. And now that put him before an even bigger problem. He could never make any of his grandmother's or his mother's dreams about his future come true. He would never become the Monseigneur. Never a doctor. Not even a teacher. Once a student was expelled from one school, he was not to be taken into another. The Tutsi community, as everyone knew, had found ways of rallying to help their youngsters—both those whose exam scores had been good though not high enough to put them among the selected few in the ethnic quota system and those who had been unjustly forced to leave school. Many were sent to the costly private schools that had begun springing up; others were slipped across the border to attend school in a neighboring country. Hutu children, though, generally lacked that kind of support, and when they failed to survive in the system, their educational careers ended.

"Papa, how can you say that you will find another school for me?"

At that reply, Emmanuel's manner had softened. "My son, you yourself one day soon will be among those who are approaching manhood, and you must understand that such is not an entirely impossible feat. It is good to have friends, good friends. And it is good to invite them to drink your beer with you. That is to say that you must also understand that among my friends there are certain ones who are conveniently placed among the educators and who comprehend our situation. For the moment, you must be patient, for as your grandmother would have said in this instance, 'The one who is patient will one day milk the heifer.'"

Richard had smiled then.

"In the meantime, in order that your days might be more profitable to yourself, your mother and I would find it good if you should choose to take the extra time with which you have been burdened and use it over in the depot."

Richard let himself slouch deeper against the wall.

Normally he would have gone to the depot already—his father was expecting another load of bananas that afternoon—but more people were moving into the center, and the bar was becoming busier than ever. Because of that, he had promised to go over and help wash glasses. The previous afternoon when he had arrived at the bar, Haricot was already at a table with a group of buddies, and he had motioned to Richard. The aura of alcohol hung strongly over the group, and Haricot had reached out toward Richard. "Whatsa matter?" he slurred. "Din'cha like the seminary?"

"Aach!" The sound came out in feigned disgust as Richard lifted an eyebrow and tipped his head.

The stocky, broad-shouldered boy grinned up at him.

"I think you would have found it better, too, to come home and work rather than to sit all day in one of those uncomfortable desks." Richard forced brightness into his answer.

Haricot and the others guffawed.

"Tha's it!" exclaimed Georges. "Stay home and work. Then ya can have beer. Lotsa it. Tha's life. A lit'l work, and ya got lotsa money for beer." Laughter, too much and too loud, followed again.

Richard looked from one to the other of the boys. Haricot pushed back on his stool. Already, at sixteen, his arms were thickly muscled. Georges hunched forward, the bottle dwarfed in his heavy hands. All of them school dropouts. But what caught Richard's attention was the extremely long nail on the little finger of each boy's left hand, the symbol of one whose education had placed his dignity above the humiliation of having to perform demeaning manual labor. "Huh-huh-huh!" His chuckle may have seemed an echo of the other boys' laughter, but he was in reality thinking of how on the secondary-school entrance exams Haricot hadn't scored high enough to be within the quota. Georges had made it, but then had to drop out after his second year because his family couldn't afford to pay his school fees. The other boys with them also had been forced to leave their studies for one reason or another, and all had gone to Kigali to find their fortunes. That's where they had been caught in a police raid and sent back home.

"Go back to your hill, they said!" Georges spoke loudly now. "What? Live in a hut like my papa?" He rolled his eyes. "Not this boy!"

In the old days, the ruling Tutsis had looked down on anyone who had to work with a hoe. Education in some ways seemed to have replaced owning cattle as a means of moving upward in social status, and many youngsters who had gone to school, even a little bit, turned their backs on the subsistence life of their parents and headed toward the city.

"We've got some contracts." Haricot leaned forward now. "Carrying stuff. When I get enough money, I'm going back to Kigali. Start my own business. Wanna come with us?"

"Haricot was at the bar this afternoon," Richard had reported to his mother that evening. "Says he's making good money as a transporter. He invited me . . ."

"You don't tie a bad goat near you." His mother's uncustomary comeback cut through his explanation.

"But, Mama, he's not that bad. He worked in Kigali on contract with a group. He's talking about going back." Richard wanted her to hear him out. "I thought maybe I could go there and stay with Annie."

"And be tempted to live with them on the streets, drinking and smoking and having nothing useful to do?" The tone of his mother's question told him quite plainly her opinion about that possibility. "Did he happen to explain exactly why he was sent home?"

"No. I thought he had just been caught with the rest in a normal raid."

When complaints became too frequent about pickpockets, petty thieves, and vagabonds, the authorities swept through Kigali, ordering everyone with neither address nor permanent employment back to their home communes. Each time the city streets were cleaned, a spate of thefts usually hit the outlying communes. People still talked of the single teacher living alone near his hill school who had been surprised one night when a gang of young ruffians burst into his house, gagged him, and tied him to his bed. Then they stripped the house—and him—bare. By morning he managed to struggle free. In his "nothing but," he slunk out of his house and called for help. A colleague loaned him clothes, making it possible for him to go back to his classroom that day and teach.

"Regardless," Régine countered, "it's better if you stay here and use the opportunity of learning the business of your father. Or perhaps you could copy your cousin who's been working with a foreign-aid project during his vacations. You could do that, you know, have a job with a development group—maybe in agriculture, maybe in reforestation."

"But, Mama." She seemed not to understand. "Have you forgotten that I don't go to school anymore?"

"You'll be going back." She spoke as if the matter were settled. "Until then, you can help your father. You don't need to go to Kigali."

"But, Mama . . ." He began again, and then his voice trailed away. What could he tell her? That he wanted to go to Kigali because he was afraid of Olive? Afraid of the way she was talking? Afraid of what she might do? Stepmothers were not to be trusted. When they hated a boy, they would stop at nothing. Seth, a classmate at the seminary, had gone totally crazy, standing by the road all day and staring into space. Poisoned, they said, by his stepmother. "It's been too many weeks already," he finally said. "Papa still hasn't worked anything out, so I thought . . ."

"That you would risk going to the city and drifting into one of those idle gangs who do nothing but drink and smoke their marijuana and imagine how they can become rich by helping themselves to someone else's belongings?" She had talked faster then. "Do you think it would make me more proud if you were to be caught by the police? Do you think I could be happy if my child were sent back to us because he had nothing better to do than to cause trouble on the city streets?"

"Not like that, Mama. I would live with Annie. She wouldn't let anything like that happen to me."

"Remember who you are, my child."

Now, sitting against the wall, he turned the question inward. "Who am I?" He looked down at his hands. Fine boned. Small. For a moment, he wished he had inherited a sturdy Hutu build like Haricot's. He was filling out, but Hutus were strong, very strong, and capable of working long and hard.

"A formidable man!" He almost grinned, remembering his grandmother's exclamations of admiration when she told the story about a Hutu who worked so hard and so fast with his hoe that he could cultivate five mountains in a day. "Formidable!" she would exclaim. "Hoe flying, up and down, turning the earth faster and faster. Running. Circling around mountain after mountain."

When his grandmother got to that part, he always imagined a man like Malachai, sweat-soaked shirt clinging to his broad back, arms swinging wildly, nonstop.

"And then his wife." His grandmother's voice would suddenly assume a tired exasperation. "In order to have an evening meal adequate for such a husband, she was obliged each day to prepare ten goats, ten cows, ten sheep, ten rabbits, ten . . ." She emphasized every *ten* in the long list. "And one entire barrel of sorghum beer and one entire barrel of oil. And the pit under that other building—it had to be at least a hundred meters deep! Yes, there are those who are created to work hard," she always concluded, "but in the end, they eat everything."

"Everything," Richard repeated to himself now, staring over the hedge and past the market with its open tables and row of thatch-roofed stalls, over the houses lining the other side of the street and the buildings beyond, past the eucalyptus giants that reached toward the sky from where his grandfather had planted them years before during an antierosion campaign, and into the distance. Sweet potatoes and sorghum filled his grandfather's fields now, planted under the careful eyes of Malachai. The calves and all the cows had been moved by his father to the ranch near Kagitumba. Suddenly, his mind cleared, and Richard clasped his hands together as he had during prayers at the seminary. He didn't have to escape by running away to work. He didn't have to listen to Olive's mockery. After all, he was his grandfather's heir. He was meant to . . .

"If the way is opened for me to return to school . . ." His half-voiced whisper formed the words more as a vow than as a prayer. "I will pray every day."

21

Kigali

"You'll need to get yourself ready." At the sound of his father's voice, Richard straightened from the wood he was chopping for the kitchen fires and lowered his ax. "That is to say that the authorities have understood our need for a solution to your problem." The dappled shadows slanting through the tree that shaded the workplace splashed across Emmanuel's face, but they did not hide his smile of triumph. "The act of cultivating friendships does, as I've told you, in time bring its own recompenses."

Richard shifted, stood his ax against the stack of dead branches, and waited for the explanation.

"Therefore, you've been designated as of tomorrow to be among those who are attending school."

So it was that Richard returned to a local classroom and with the other students prepared to write the entrance examination for a regular secondary-school program. The weeks slipped by, and the date for the examination was nearing. "There have been words again at the house of the other one." He sat in the shade, the latest Catholic youth paper open on his knee, when this latest bearer of news swished into the yard. "The husband has been loudly reproached for neglecting her care." The voice, its nasal pitch sharp and penetrating, continued detailing the latest outburst. "She accuses him of bringing everything to this side and leaving her with nothing."

That woman!" Richard's under-the-breath complaint included both Olive and the one who had come to fill his mother's ears with what she'd heard. Olive's tirades frequently became the talk of the town. "Everything goes to your idol!" That was her latest theme, which the gossips tossed back and forth among themselves. The accusation did have its basis in some truth. Emmanuel did confide his business income to Régine. Rwandan women, though expected to maintain a respectfully discreet attitude, are appreciated for business acumen, and Régine possessed an astute sense for helping her husband improve his business interests. "Always complaining and whining!" Richard slapped the paper closed and with his thumbnail cut a series of close zigzags along its spine. "Yet she rules the grandparents' place like a tyrant queen, and she installs her ugly sisters and cousins to make sure that she gets more than her share." Family chief though Richard was, his father would, as long as he lived, be the one to administer the family herds and property.

"She's gone so far as to wish the death of the big one there."

Richard saw the woman's head bob in his direction, but he pretended to be engrossed in his paper. *I knew it! I told Papa!* His thoughts raced with the abrupt knowledge that this visit was not intended as mere idle gossip. This was a direct warning. *She won't stop now!* Suddenly, he was afraid. More afraid than he had ever been before. Olive hated him. Stepmothers always hated the sons of their husband's other wives. They always looked for ways to get at the boys before the boys became old enough to pay them back for their earlier mistreatment. Olive wanted him dead. She would find a poison maker. She would not stop now. She would somehow find a maker of the mysterious powder, and she would have it slipped into his food.

The next evening, Richard slumped on one of the straight-backed wooden dining-room chairs, head tilted forward. He rolled and unrolled the corners of his khaki school shirt between his finger. "She hates me." He did not look up. "Papa, Olive hates me!"

"As I've told you before, you are not to think such thoughts." Emmanuel spoke gruffly.

"She does, Papa. She wants me dead."

"She may have a tongue that says too much, but . . ."

"Papa." Richard looked up at his father now, his eyes dull and round. "She'll not stop until she's had me poisoned!"

"Richard! I've told you before, and for the last time I repeat, that whatever Olive's faults may seem to be, you are not to speak against her like that."

"But, Papa."

Lips tightly closed, Emmanuel regarded his son.

"She wants my life."

Poisonings happened. Everyone knew that. In Rwanda, they had always happened. That's one of the reasons his grandmother had taught him never to eat with a family that was not of their own intimate circle. Sometimes an individual, like the mother of one of his classmates, suddenly dropped dead after eating or drinking something into which an invisible powder had been mixed. "Her boy was doing too well at school." The neighbors shook their heads knowingly. "And that one—she let too many know about it. Someone put poison in her water gourd." To protect their families from the rampant jealousies, some parents never spoke the names of their schoolchildren in the presence of their neighbors, nor did they ever mention the name of the schools to which they had gone.

"It pays to be discreet," Régine often warned Richard. "No matter how smiling and how friendly a neighbor may seem to be, you can never read the true feelings of another's heart. The hand that embraces you can carry a dagger up its sleeve."

Though deaths did occur from these suspected poisonings, more frequently, the victim—usually a student—became inexplicably ill, exhibiting strange and undefinable physical or even mental symptoms. Modern medicine routinely failed to find the causes or to treat such cases, and the families usually resorted to calling in a traditional healer. It took months, sometimes years, for the herbal potions or powders to purge the system.

KILL THY NEIGHBOR

As to who, precisely, were the initiates into the ancient mysteries of preparing and administrating the poisons, no one was prepared to say. They worked clandestinely, like a traditional mafia guild, and had always been thought of as criminals. But they were to be found by anyone whose jealousies had passed the bounds of tolerance.

"I'll have to leave, or that woman will poison me." Richard spoke his fears to his mother now.

"Don't think like that, my child."

"She hates me, Mama. She hates me." Richard's face twisted. "She could find someone, like the jealous ones do. Mama . . ." He told her about Seth, how he had been taken home to a traditional healer. And about Adiel, one of the top students in the senior class, who had become deathly ill. Poisoned, they said.

"Such thoughts will do you no good."

"But, Mother . . ."

"Your father will see that nothing happens."

To please his mother, Richard masked his feelings and let the matter drop. With the others in his class, he wrote the admittance exam into secondary school. Meanwhile, he continued to work at the bar after his classes. From time to time, Haricot came in with his buddies. "Nosomuch work anymore," the burly young Hutu complained. "But you wou'n't know 'bout tha. You're your papa's *umuzungu.*"

Richard cringed inside. Being called a White was not a compliment, and he hurried past the table, pretending he had not heard. When he got home, Shema met him in the courtyard. "Olive's been fighting with Papa again and saying all sorts of mean things about Mama and about you."

"Does Mama know?"

Shema nodded.

"Then pay no mind to what Olive says." Richard smiled at his sister. "That one is all noise and no sense, and Papa won't let her do anything to any of us."

Despite his brave words to his sister, Richard lay awake long into the night. The next morning, he was up early. Quietly he removed a brick from the wall of his room and fished out a wad of bills he had stashed behind it—tips and other earnings from the bar that he had been saving. He shoved the brick back, shoved the money into a pocket of his school bag, dressed as usual, then hurried out into the morning as if he were on his way to school. On the other side of the market, he turned to the right instead of to the left and broke into a sprint toward the big aqua-painted commercial building. He found one of the company drivers. Bargained. Ten minutes later, he was atop a pickup load of sorghum, bound for Kigali.

"Richard!" his big sister Annie exclaimed when he arrived at her door in Kigali that afternoon. "What's the news? Is everything all right with the family?"

"The news is good," he began in the usual response, "except . . ." And then he told her about Olive's threats. "Annie." He looked into his big sister's eyes. "I'm afraid. I had to run away. I'm afraid of what that woman might do. Please!" A chalkiness dulled his dark cheeks.

"Your family will be very worried when you don't come home today—especially if things are as you say."

"Send my father a message. Tell him not to worry, but plead for me. Tell him I don't want to study there anymore. Tell him that since I've already written the exam, I want to be here. Tell him anything. But don't tell him the real reason. Don't say it's because I'm afraid Olive will poison me."

Annie listened quietly.

"My father wouldn't believe that. He wouldn't listen to me earlier. He won't believe the danger now. He'll make me come home. When my mother hears that I'm here, she'll understand. Please! Annie?"

"You can outdistance that which is running after you," Annie said, quoting a well-known proverb, "but not that which is running inside you."

"Then you understand. You know that I had to come."

She nodded. "I'll find someone this evening and send word to your family that you have arrived safely and that I wish for you to remain here with Fredy and me.

22

Poisoned

When Emmanuel's latest vehicle, a battered green pickup, rattled into Annie's yard some weeks later, Richard felt a sudden panic. *He's come to get me!* his thoughts screamed. *But I won't go home. I won't!* Shoving his feelings down and masking them with a smile, he went to greet his father. Once the polite formulas of inquiring about the news of the family had been exhausted and the adults had adjourned themselves to visit in the living room, Richard disappeared with the other boys and kept himself out of sight in a back room. The others came and went, tending to their normal afternoon activities.

"Sha, Richard!" Evarice, a distant cousin who was living with Annie so he could attend a city school, bounced into the room. "Your name's on the list. I just heard your papa telling Annie. You passed the exam!"

"Is it true?"

"It's true!" Evarice held out his hand, and the boys slapped palms and then clasped hands in an exuberant handshake. "You're on the list of those who've been selected to go to school."

The next morning, Richard gathered his things and gladly went home with his father. Two weeks later, he arrived on the campus of one of the largest Catholic secondary schools in the country. From that point, his life continued an upward progress. He was elected chief of his class. He earned his first-aid certificate and became an active member and officer of the school's Red Cross Brigade. And to make good his earlier promise, he joined a charismatic prayer group that met each evening after their study hour.

"What do we pray about this evening, Cardinal?" a friend asked, using the nickname Richard's faithful prayer habits had earned him.

"Good results in our exams and safe travels to our homes for the long school vacation." Richard always had a number of requests to address to the distant and powerful, yet fearsome, Trinity whom the church taught them to worship in place of the Imana of his ancestors. "And success in our vacation jobs."

He had been selected to work with the CARE International reforestation project in his home commune. When school was out and he arrived to be with his parents, he went about his job very seriously and was up early each morning to be on time to supervise a team of contract workers. His responsibilities included checking the positioning and depth and width of the holes they dug for planting the young trees and verifying that they'd completed their day's quota. While he had been away at school, his father had built the annex. "Your own apartment," Emmanuel said, handing Richard the key. "So you won't disturb the younger ones with your comings and goings."

The days passed quickly. Richard came home exceptionally tired one evening and closed himself in his room. He had already brought in the few of his grandfather's possessions that had come to him and had arranged them to his liking. The flute on a shelf by the window, the spear and the baton in the corner behind the old man's stool, and the hunting bow and its arrows in another corner. "I wonder . . ."

His eyes traced the sparse geometric design carved into the seasoned deep red surface of the baton's ironlike wood, and he remembered his grandfather sitting on his stool presiding over family matters while he held the old baton. In those days, the carved stick had almost made him afraid and never, except at his grandfather's order, would he ever have touched it. "The spirits are very jealous of those who remain among the living," his grandfather had warned. He had passed the warning on to his own little brother and sisters—there had been another two sisters and a little brother since his mother had returned—and his cousins. "The spirits don't want just anybody tampering with what they've left behind. They get jealous and do things to people who make them angry. If you ever take Grandfather's things without permission . . ."

In some ways, he wanted the beliefs in the ancestral spirits to be true. The old teachings said that at death the shadow part of a person left the physical body, mysteriously transforming so that it could go to live in the spirit world deep within the great volcanoes. Though it changed form, it kept its human character and could be very unpredictable—getting angry and taking out its spite on the humans who for one reason or another continued to offend it. But if it was as the family elders said, then his grandfather was near Imana and would help to protect him. For the living, Imana the creator was distant and shadowy and fearsome. He was pictured as being impossible to be approached by mere humans. The ancient hero Ryangombe, who had become chief of the spirits, though, had access to the divine presence.

Something like the Virgin Mary and God, Richard was thinking. All you had to do was say "Be with God" to Ryangombe, and he would carry the prayer to Imana. And Imana might be convinced to intervene on a person's behalf. *I wonder . . .* In some ways the ancestral spirits did resemble the Catholic saints. *Is there really a difference? Or is it that the old Rwandan religion and the Christian church simply have different teachings about the same thing?* Christians and those who practiced the ancient cults both used the same word for the all-powerful sovereign deity, and many parents, both Christian and animist, gave their children names that either ended in *imana,* as did the name of their President Habyarimana, or that alluded to the powers of the supreme god. Richard's own Rwandan name, *Siboniyo,* linked him with God, but it did not indicate which way—ancient or Christian— would lead him to the truth about that mysterious, far-off deity.

The next day at work, Richard still felt tired. Since childhood he had suffered from periodic bouts of malaria, but like a mild flu, they were nothing more than an inconvenience that, if treated soon enough, passed in a few days, leaving no trace. On the following day, his energy level was even lower. He forced himself to stay on the job. Even though Emmanuel provided for his school fees, supplies, and uniforms and could give him everything he needed, he insisted that Richard earn his own money for the more fashionable clothes and other luxuries that he wanted. For that, Richard respected his father.

Several more days passed. Richard did not get better, nor did he feel much worse except that his skin had become unusually dry and scaly. Skin creams and butter did not help. The following week, he had no appetite.

"Do you think I should go to the dispensary?" he asked his mother.

"Wait," she suggested. "We'll see how this goes."

The days brought no change. A few days later, an old woman appeared at their gate, a worn cloth drooping from her shoulders. Tattered skirts draped her body, their ragged edges trailing above her calloused feet. His mother invited her in. "This is the one," she said, pointing toward Richard.

"You're sick, I can tell." The woman peered toward him. "Come to my house at sunrise tomorrow. I have the medicine that you need."

Early the next morning, he pushed through the narrow opening in an overgrown hedge and stood before a mud-daubed hut. The hut's walls leaned at angles under the old thatch, and the door had to be lifted and scuffed back on its rusty hinges. He waited while the woman bustled about, setting an old, dull gray clay pot over her fire and pouring in a dark liquid. "Drink this," she said at last, holding out a cupful of the warmed substance. "Then go stand over there." She pointed toward a space behind the hut. "Keep your face toward the rising sun, and vomit."

The brew was bitter and as foul tasting as anything he could imagine. He gagged. Then forced it down, swallow after difficult swallow.

"Vomit!" The old woman stood beside him, waiting.

He gagged again. Nothing came.

"Here." She snapped a stem from a scraggled weed. "Push this against the back of your throat."

Richard wretched.

The woman regarded the ground. "Aaahhhh!" she exclaimed, straightening and turning so that Richard could see the sparkle in her beady eyes. "You've been poisoned!" Her laugh sounded like a triumphant cackle. "Poisoned!" She studied the ground again. "I see that you were given banana juice into which had been put a poisonous powder. Come back again tomorrow."

"I told you, Mama!" Richard's eyes flashed when he returned home. "Olive hates me. She's the one responsible. She . . ." He felt the heat rise along his neck, and he flung himself around, staring in the direction of his grandfather's place. "That woman is trying to kill me!"

"Tell me, did the healer have any other instructions for you?"

"She said for me to return tomorrow."

"Do as she says."

By the time Emmanuel came that evening, Richard's anger had settled, solid and cold. "That woman has tried to kill me."

"No!" Emmanuel jumped to his feet. "I don't know what has happened to you. I don't know what is making you sick. I don't know if anyone is responsible for doing anything to make you sick. But you are not to accuse anyone without first having proof. Olive is innocent!"

"Papa!"

"I repeat myself. Olive is innocent, and you are to remember that."

Emmanuel turned, and without pronouncing any farewells, left the house. Richard knew without being told that his father had gone to Olive.

Richard returned to the healer the next morning. On the fourth morning, he vomited blood. "Good! Good! Good!" The hook of a tooth that stood alone in her upper jaw clacked against the woman's good lower teeth. "Now we can begin to have some success with your case. Now you can be treated in a fashion that will terminate the problem that has caused your sickness. Come again tomorrow, and I will have a quantity of the medicine that you will need."

Richard returned the next day with a bottle, into which the woman poured an equally foul-looking liquid. "You will need to have this every morning, and gradually it will clean away the poison that has made you sick. Warm it as I have been warming the other, drink it, and then stand toward the rising sun and vomit. Afterward, eat your breakfast as usual."

When classes resumed for the new school year, Richard arrived on campus with a plastic jerrycan full of his medication. Early each morning, instead of going to prayers, he slipped down to the kitchen. No one knew what he did except for the cook, who heated his daily cupful of the dark brew. Then he would go out, alone, beyond the bushes that enclosed the campus. And wretch. And feel miserable. And wish that someone could be there to comfort him. But he dared not share his secret with anyone. Especially not the teachers. Traditional cures were not to be spoken about.

He lost weight.

He felt weak.

The tough, scaly surface on his arms and his legs continued to itch.

His grades fell.

He worried about his exams.

Each morning, though, he dutifully faced the rising sun, whose warming rays, the woman had assured him, would stimulate the nausea when he imbibed his cure. At the end of each month, he went home, and she refilled his jerrycan. By Christmas the itching lessened. After Easter he began to feel less tired. He scraped through the final exams, but never in his life had he received such low scores. From then on, he spent his school vacations with his sister Annie in Kigali.

"A stepmother who feels threatened by the sons of her husband's other wives will stop at nothing," he confided to Annie. "Olive failed this time. I don't intend to give her another chance."

By his senior year he had fully recovered and earned a government scholarship to the school of medicine at the National University in Butare. By then, good highways constructed with foreign aid linked north and south and east and west; several foreign development projects stimulated the economy; and, on the surface at least, the country seemed to have smoothed over its ethnic problems.

23

Opposite Directions

"The signs were there, if we'd just . . ."

Richard faced his boyhood friend Frank. Too much had happened. After his first year of medicine, the FPR had attacked. That was October 1990 when he was at the ranch. He fled the invaders only to be arrested by the army. After being freed, he worked with the Red Cross, burying those killed in the fighting and treating the injured. The academic year was canceled because of the war. Now with the cease-fire, he and Frank were home and planning to build their houses.

"Remember . . ."

Frank nodded.

Tense. That's what life had become. Multi-party elections had been promised. Cease-fire terms had given the FPR forces the area to their north. Displaced Hutus sheltered around the commercial sector. Long-time Tutsi residents kept a low profile.

"They won't be satisfied until they're the government," Frank said.

During the eighties, President Habyarimana's government had put down an attempted coup. Then there were the student strikes. Rumor blamed them on outside forces trying to destabilize the government.

"Organized by the Tutsis," charged the Hutus.

The Tutsis claimed innocence.

At one school where Hutus from the president's home area dominated the administration, Tutsi leaders were accused of organizing a takeover. Some had older children at the school; others had family members on the teaching and cafeteria staff.

"You can trap students in two places," the Tutsis reportedly declared. "In the cafeteria and in the classroom." So, according to the stories, they decided their cooks should slip sand into the rice each evening and cut back the amount of sugar being put into the porridge in the morning, and they asked their teachers to see that grade reports had certain points missing. Then they told their children to quietly complain about all this to the other students—especially to a clique of older Hutu boys known for their rowdiness—and suggest that *measures* be taken.

At supper one evening, the Hutu clique waited until last to go through line. They collected their bowls of rice and beans and went to their table. Hardly had they settled to their places when one jumped to his feet. "Sand again!" He drew back his hand and hurled his bowl upside down onto the table. His tablemates copied him. Food flew in every direction. "All right, everyone!" he shouted. "Who's coming with us?

Quiet fell. Then, at his order, everyone trooped after him down the road past the faculty homes. Up and down the road they marched, singing "Onward Christian Soldiers." At last, they were led back to the campus, but during the night, warnings circulated through the dormitories. Anyone not cooperating in the morning could expect consequences. If not immediately, then in some unknown future their ears would be cut off, their eyes gouged out, and their tongues ripped from their mouths. At first light, every student obediently went to the campus square.

Younger girls huddled in fearful clumps.

Older girls sat in resigned silence.

Most of the boys seemed uninterested in being present.

But all sat. Trapped. Between orders from the school to go to class or else suffer consequences that might include expulsion and the graphic threats from the ringleaders. No one was to attend class until the school met their thirty-three grievances, ranging from giving them more sugar to removing certain teachers. The strike continued for five days.

All the while, the Tutsi students, following their elders' advice, mumbled about the stupidity of certain student elements who thought this was the way to solve problems. In the end, the military was brought in. Most of the students, among them all the Tutsis, willingly returned to class. The Hutu ringleaders were punished, one even being expelled, for leading out in the strike. Afterward, a flurry of letters, many coming from modest Hutu parents who had been visited by their Tutsi pastors, complained about the school's lack of control.

"Whoever manipulated the strikes," Frank was saying, "the extremists on both sides want only one thing—power!"

Richard made no further reply. What he wanted most was a settled life. In the meantime, he had chosen the perfect place for his house—the old calf pasture behind the protection of the tall, white-trunked eucalyptus break his grandfather had planted. Frank was building his in town. "The year I finish my studies, I'll be married," Richard had promised his parents. Eighteen was the traditional age, but students preferred to complete their education before taking on the responsibility of a family.

Olive still lived at the old home place and could remain as long as Richard's father wanted. As the youngest child, Emmanuel, by tradition, had stayed on to care for his aging parents and was for all practical purposes the real owner of everything. Yet he could sell nothing, neither herds nor property, without first consulting Richard and afterward giving him a token from the transactions.

Twice Richard had met Haricot. Still carrying heavy loads when he could find someone to hire him, he had become husky and well-muscled, with a body that could turn the eye of any girl. But, as Richard noted to his mother, his disposition seemed even more surly.

"Not much paying work these days," Régine commented. "He and his group sit too much around a calabash. Drinking. Smoking marijuana. Like the rest who've had just enough schooling to lose interest in creating a respectful life. In the old days, the vassals may have slaved for their lords, but at least they did respectful work, and they raised respectful families, and with patience they sometimes worked their way to become owners of cattle. These young ones . . ." The years since her return had fleshed out Régine's face, giving it the softness of middle-aged understanding. "With poorly fed stomachs, they risk becoming slaves to anyone who promises them a little something. Is it true?" she asked, interrupting her own train of thought, "what we hear about the politicians using the street boys for their party meetings?"

"It's true." Time had also matured Richard, and the dark lines of a mustache traced his upper lip. "Huh-huh-huh." His throaty half-laugh had assumed a rich baritone that reminded everyone of his grandfather. "Very resourceful, those politicians. They find someone like Haricot's friend Georges, someone who's a leader on the streets because he has a bit more education than the others, someone who speaks and understands enough French to make his way with almost anyone. They'll slip him ten thousand (about $75) and tell him to bring his friends to their political rally on such and such a night. He knows exactly what they want. He rounds up the boys he can find, spends a couple thousand for drinks for everyone, then takes them to the meeting. Whenever the speaker pauses, the boys cheer. Loud and long.

" 'Ach,' say the curious ones who've drifted in to listen. 'Hear those cheers. Whatever this one is saying, it must be good.' And when the supporters circulate to sign up new party members, they sign."

"That makes me afraid." Régine examined her close-clipped nails and carefully rubbed a dark trace from one. "I'm afraid that too many of our people, especially our young ones, are no longer masters of their own consciences and that they have become willing to sell themselves to do no matter what anyone asks." She was still speaking toward her lap, her voice low. "Your friend Haricot. The thousands upon thousands like him, sitting and waiting for their fortune. My son." She looked at Richard now. "I'm so glad for the effort your father has made to prepare you for a future that will bring honor to our ancestors and make you a man worthy of the name."

That October when school reopened, Richard returned to the university. The following year, he received his degree in human biology and moved to the level that would make him a Doctor of General Medicine. Student life was good. With his government bursary and the income from certain investments he'd made with his father, he bought a car, he dressed in the latest campus fashion, and on his free afternoons he took his friends wherever they wanted to go. He was in charge of his own life. Sometimes he went to church—if there was an important visitor or something else of special interest. As for God— He had disappeared with the ancestors. And Richard felt he no longer needed the prayers he had so religiously repeated at secondary school in fulfillment of his vow.

Someone mentioned a document circulating among certain Hutus that allegedly had been seized years earlier from a Tutsi refugee. Supposedly it showed Tutsi strategies aimed against Hutus, with the ulterior goal of gaining control of specific territories outside the country. If you can't replace an elected Hutu, it purportedly said in part, make a friend of him. They're gourmands. Offer them presents, especially beer and money. We have plenty. Know that the Hutu is created to serve, so keep them in an inferiority complex. They're naive. If it serves our purposes, fight against their enemies. They'll appreciate you for that. Organize youth groups that, if other means fail, can be used for terrorism. Use the pact of blood for the Hutu mass. We know the ineffectiveness of this pact and have violated it in the past without any harm. And, finally, if necessary, give our women to them in marriage because the Hutus have a hard time resisting their beauty.

Whatever the reliability of the document, a definite dilemma had been created during the war because of those caught in a situation similar to the one cited in the document's last point. Many Hutu military officers had Tutsi wives. A number of Hutu politicians also had Tutsi wives. Richard understood their predicament. With the building ethnic polarization, he felt himself being pulled in two very opposite directions.

24

Engaged

"Ach! Richard!" Shema exclaimed. "What have you ever known about such things as fashion?"

"I know what I like when I see it. And I like these." He held a folded pair of trousers and a shirt, also neatly folded. The late December warmth hung comfortably in the evening, and the wavering light from the kerosene lamp was almost cheerful. "Besides, Aline says . . ."

"Who's this Aline anyhow, whose wisdom seems to take priority in every conversation we endeavor to hold?" With an exaggerated breath, Shema hefted her shoulders.

Despite her mock disgust, Richard read more meaning into his sister's words than she intended to show. "She has good taste, like you," he said quietly. "You . . ." He started to say that she did not need to be jealous but realized in time that this was not something he should say. Especially not at that moment. "You'll be glad when you no longer have the responsibility of all my washing and mending and ironing and cleaning and having to always tell me what I should wear."

"Richard!"

"Well?"

KILL THY NEIGHBOR

"Oh! You know!"

He did know. Since she had first learned home chores from their grandmother, Shema had always taken it as her personal responsibility to see that everything of his was clean and in order. Growing up in their grandparents' home, they had shared a special brother-sister friendship and had solidly stood together in their common need to protect each other and Marie-Pierre from Olive.

"I know." He smiled now. "I also know that Aline reminds me very much of you." He glanced appreciatively at his sister's long, oval face, with its high cheekbones and fine features mirroring their mother's elegant beauty. "You yourself did admit she is at least pretty and nice and that she knows how to dress."

"But . . ."

"Then you approve of this outfit for my visit to her parents with Jean Baptiste."

"My dear big brother." Shema laughed now. "Of course I would not think of trying to change your mind. But . . ." Her eyes teased up at him. "What if her parents refuse?"

"They wouldn't!" Richard's voice rose as if the idea were unthinkable.

Two days later, on the morning after New Year's Day, he drove from the temporary home where his parents had moved to distance themselves from the destabilizing FPR incursions, heading his white Peugeot toward the home village of Aline's parents. Beside him sat Jean Baptiste, his father's long-time friend and boyhood companion, who delivered a running commentary on the passing countryside, noting how it became more hilly toward the south and how from a certain rise the lake appeared to be a flat, gray-white arm stretching toward the distant hills. All Aline's family—aunts, uncles, cousins and distant cousins, brothers and sisters, as well her parents—were waiting when they arrived. After they had presented the expected cases of beer and Fanta, and after the formal welcomes had been made, Jean Baptiste launched into the explanation of their visit.

"The one whom I am representing," he said, alluding to Emmanuel, "that one has sent me to tell you that the one who is going to replace him in the future has received an education and that he sees this same one is now big enough, and he has requested that I ask you if there is the possibility that you would be willing to give us the one whom you also have educated on your part." The Kinyarwanda Jean Baptiste spoke wound through many allusions. Aline's father sat across from them, but he made no move to respond. Another man, the equal of Jean Baptiste, who had been chosen by Aline's father as spokesman for their family, now stood.

"We have lots of children," the spokesman replied. "Would you like to take them all?"

"We would like to take them all," responded Jean Baptiste, "but if we were to take all of your children, then you would be left alone."

The two men continued bantering back and forth while the others enjoyed both the verbal skills of the two orators and the drinks that were being served nonstop. "Perhaps you would like to take Jean Louis," suggested the spokesman, pointing to one of the boys sitting across the room.

"Yes, we would like Jean Louis," agreed Jean Baptiste, "because we see that he is capable of taking care of the family, but we see that our son Richard is also capable of that; therefore, it is not Jean Louis whom we need."

The discussions continued, following the traditionally prescribed formula for requesting a woman's hand in marriage. All of Aline's family were present, but only Jean Baptiste and Richard himself represented his family. Jean Baptiste spoke in a careful Kinyarwanda, being mindful to not offend anyone, either by the manner in which he made his request or in the manner in which he turned aside the ones suggested by his counterpart. "We have need of someone who can care for the milk and who is capable with using a broom," he continued, making allusions to the work reserved for Rwandan women. A man would never think of cleaning the house after his marriage, nor of caring for the milk or churning butter in the crook-necked churning gourd.

"Then we are in agreement to find you a girl," the spokesman offered after more discussion, "but the dowry has never been given for the mother of that girl, so therefore the girl must be the dowry for her mother."

Richard understood that it was their way of asking for a double dowry payment.

"Two dowries, twice times eight cows?" Jean Baptiste countered. "No. We've come purely with the intention of finding the one with whom this one corresponds." His full reply discreetly circumvented the dowry idea so that no one could infer that the young woman for whom they had come was being purchased from her family. At last, the other spokesman agreed that the family would agree to give them a young woman.

"But who is it?" he asked. "Is it one of these?" Two tiny girls were brought forward, one a toddler, the other, a babe in arms, who was crying.

"Is that one really capable of preparing food?" Jean Baptiste asked, hiding the question in a burst of flowery Kinyarwanda so that no one could take anything he said as an insult against the baby who was being offered.

"Why do you refuse our girls?" the other replied. "Your boy? Isn't he wanting two girls?" At that point, Aline was brought in with one of her sisters from the extended family. Jean Baptiste lapsed into poetry, weaving rhythmic syllables and rhyme into spontaneous praise of both, alluding to their beauty, speaking of cattle and wealth and goodness, speaking of Richard. "But that one there," he finally said, pointing to Aline, "I see that is the one who is right."

Richard stood and went toward her, reaching out both his hands to touch her arms. He lightly brushed her cheeks with his, first one side, then the other, but their lips did not meet. A kiss? In public? He could not risk such brashness. That might offend some in her family. "Be with your husband." He spoke the traditional expression conveying his wish that she be his wife.

"I am satisfied," she replied.

High, wavering cries, the *inpundu*, filled the room as all the aunts and girl cousins trilled out their joy, and then the two of them took their places side by side as a recognized couple. Jean Baptiste presented a hoe to Aline's family as symbol of Richard's seriousness to provide for the woman they had asked to be his wife, and a case of beer, symbolic of the special prepared homemade beer used throughout the centuries to seal the marriage contact. Details of the dowry would be settled later, but they had already agreed it would be a sum of money and not the customary gift of cows. On their wedding day, though, her family would be presented with three cows as symbol of the dowry that had already been sent ahead. Afterward, the wedding party would go to the commune office for their civil marriage, then to the Catholic church, where their union would be blessed by the priest, and then after the reception they would drive home to the house that he was building on his grandfather's lands, since the wedding night must always be spent at the home place of the groom's parents.

That night, after he had recounted the day's events to his parents, he sat alone in the living room with Emmanuel. "Papa," he asked, "What do you make of our new politics?"

Emmanuel contemplated his almost-empty bottle of beer and drew a long breath. "Many men have been using an excess of many words, and that is especially true now with the unrelenting use of this word *democracy*, which apparently they seem to understand as the freedom to do whatever they want; to get whatever they want."

"And the men of the church—why are so many of them involved in these political matters?"

Emmanuel tipped his head as if his son were adding an idea that went beyond their normal conversation. "What is it that you mean by that?"

"Well . . ." Suddenly, Richard was remembering the long drive home when he had been expelled from the seminary and the cryptic, uncomplimentary remarks his father had directed over his shoulder at the priests who had sent him from the school. At the time, that had given him some comfort. His father had blamed them. Not him. In a vague way, he also admired his father and his firm stand against the decrees of the church regarding Olive, as much as he himself despised and distrusted the woman. Because of ethnic tensions, Emmanuel had taken her as his wife. Then, when the tensions had eased, he had not casually dismissed her, as the church insisted he do, and risked leaving her to the caprices that could await an abandoned woman.

"I've heard that in the past a certain priest at one of the big Catholic schools was the most influential man in the country."

"Ah yes," Emmanuel replied. "I know the one you mean—years and years in the same school, probably knew more people in the country than any other single person. His word would naturally reach the level of having much influence, since the colonial government used the Catholics to operate most of the schools. Many of his former students being among those with some education suddenly found themselves with a country to run, and, of course, they would ask for advice from the ones they admired among those who had educated them. Who else would they have to turn to in such matters?"

"That I understand," Richard agreed. "But today? Even at the university we hear that to join the FPR and fight for the return of a Tutsi regime, all you have to do is cross the border and contact Pastor So-and-so, and he will put you in touch with the ones you need to know. And we hear about priests and pastors who use their status and their connections to receive clandestine arms shipments for the FPR and who even stock them in *holy* places, all the while professing to be the dispensers of God's Word."

"You know how it has always been among our people—the man to be admired is the one who can manipulate others with his words and take the position that life has offered him and turn it to the best interests of himself and his own."

"But don't you find that a contradiction—even wrong? Men call themselves representatives of God and teach that we must love our neighbor, and then they themselves become instruments to work for the destruction of that same neighbor."

Emmanuel's lips twisted into what may have been intended as a smile. "Perhaps that is among the reasons why you see me as I am," he replied.

That had been in January. Now it was April. Since then, his family had moved back to their ancestral village.

When he had dropped Aline and the others off in Kigali for the Easter vacation, Richard had expected to come, arrange for the finishing work on the house, enjoy a few lazy days with Frank, and spend some time with his parents, and then return to campus, complete his medical studies, and be married in August. But on Wednesday, President Habyarimana was killed when his plane was downed. And now . . .

Since he had come from Frank's, everyone in the family had cloistered in the compound, moving like mechanical shadows who spoke as if their voices belonged to some detached distance. Or didn't speak. His own restless steps had carried him around the cattle sheds, into the stockrooms and out, and into the house. Sometimes he crossed paths with the others; usually, he simply wandered back into his own quarters in the annex and invariably found himself taking up his photo album—for what real motive, he had no idea. He simply did it. And now it was Wednesday again, and the album again lay on his knees, open to that favorite photo of Aline. Shema sat across from him. But neither talked any longer of photos or fashions or weddings.

"Richard." His sister's voice sounded flat. "It's finished for us."

"Don't say that! God willing . . ."

"God? Imana?" She cut him short. "Where has He been for all those hundreds of thousands of others? Do we deserve Him any more than they?"

He had no answer. That's when he started talking about going back to Butare and had asked her to wash his shirts.

25

Interahamwe!

Thursday morning dawned sunny and warm. A perfect day as far as the weather was concerned, and toward midmorning, large white cumulus billows had built themselves into beautiful cloud ships that rode full sail above the soft blue horizon. Normally, it would have been the sort of April day to go out, visit with friends, and check the progress on his house, but, instead, Richard, as well as everyone in the family, wandered about, dull-eyed and silent. He tried to make himself seem busy but was unable to settle down to do anything specific. Earlier he'd helped Malachai with the cows. That is to say, he had gone in when Malachai was milking.

"Mpatie should freshen soon."

Richard nodded at the news about the large, dappled cow but said nothing.

"As soon as I have finished, I'll see what news there is at the market."

"Good."

Throughout the morning, Malachai had come and gone. Toward noon, he left again. Then it was that Richard had heard the distant clamor. He tensed. Listening. Beyond the buildings. Where the road wandered through a series of banana patches. A growing whining and whirring like thousands and thousands of wild bees swarming. His stomach squeezed into a sick knot, and when he tried to swallow, the walls of his throat behaved like worn pieces of sandpaper.

"No! Not again! Not . . . !" His mind wanted to build a wall. To block out the noise. To push it a thousand kilometers away. "Those . . . those . . ." He could not find words loathsome enough to fit what was happening.

Every day. Since the president's plane had been downed. The rabble. Maddened by the inflammatory rhetoric of political masterminds. *In revenge for a president's death?* His thoughts burned with horrors the RFI, BBC, and VOA reports painted of what had been happening in other parts of their country. Their little country. Their beautiful little country. At one time, the British, the Belgians, and the Germans had all argued over it, each wanting it for a colony—the British so it would form a link in their Cape-to-Cairo railroad, the Belgians to gain access to Lake Victoria, the Germans for their Central African Empire. And now. He matched the sickening reports with the isolated horrors of what had happened already in their own commune.

The noise pushed nearer.

He could make no more sense of what was happening than could anyone else. The half-trained militia. Drug-deadened drifters. Simple hill peasants. Others whose consciences had become hazed. Those who hated, who were jealous, who could not tolerate someone because of the good things that he had or because of some long-past misdeed, either real or imagined. Fed with beer and with words that were used like keys to turn on a vicious hate, they were sent out on their murderous missions. Then, once heady with the letting of blood, they mowed like death machines through the countryside toward targets named in clandestine meetings, toward those marked for annihilation. Individuals, families, entire settlements. Sacrificed. Because of hate. Because of an enemy. Because of the tribal blood that coursed their veins.

"It's finished for us!"

The cold panic of Shema's prediction the evening before throbbed in his ears now, and a half-numb, half-tingling sensation spread around the back of his head, over his shoulders, and down his back. Momentarily, he wondered what it would feel like to die. To become one of the ancestors, a floating spirit inhabiting some mysterious place down deep inside a volcano. And then to come back, invisible and meddlesome, settling scores with those who perpetrated this horrible rampage, making them suffer, suffer, and suffer some more for their unspeakable misdeeds. Or, perchance sometimes, to help those you'd once loved.

Maybe. He paused thoughtfully. *Maybe the Catholic fathers are right. Maybe our souls do go to purgatory. To be purified. And then to Paradise.*

The sounds seemed nearer.

Of course, if anything should happen to me . . . He closed his eyes momentarily. *Aline would pray for me. Every day. That my time in purgatory would be shortened. And my mother. And . . .* His thoughts swung crazily. He'd go for Aline. Maybe that evening. They'd go back to Butare. No matter what his mother said. He had to get away. It was too dangerous to stay. He had friends who would help. He'd find them. As soon as it was dark again.

The distant noise suddenly ballooned in a shrieking, screaming, yelling confusion mowing along the road toward the market.

Interahamwe!

He didn't know who called out the warning. Or exactly what happened next. Only that a sudden windmill of panic scattered through the courtyard. Everyone. Frantic. Running. Disappearing. Each toward his or her own secret hiding place. With one horror-laden glance through the fence, he saw the mob advancing along the street beyond the market, and in that split second, everything registered itself on his brain as if he had observed it on a video safely boxed in some distant television screen. Details chiseled into his memory. Layers of banana leaves. Menacing. Green. Flouncing around heads. Daubs of kaolin, that prodigious white clay often used in ceremonies of earlier times, smeared features, and crisscrossed naked torsos. Spears. Machetes. Hoes. Clubs. Hefted in attack mode. Shrieks and screams. Echoing. Reechoing. Saturating the air. And through the din, one word pierced. One clear, distinct, blood-chilling word.

"Traitors!"

Richard's feet pounded wildly against the cement courtyard, careening him around the house and through the open door of the kitchen hut. Instinctively, he grabbed the razor blade, the sharp emergency implement that he'd never stopped carrying since his Red Cross service during the first months of the civil war. Then he was digging his fingers, his toes, into the rough adobe walls of the kitchen, clawing upward, bracing himself, whittling with the razor blade, slicing through strand after strand of the shriveled cording that twined lengths of bamboo into a solid ceiling.

He heard and at the same time didn't hear how the screaming broke into a babble of individual voices. Silently he berated the one who had laced the bamboo in so tightly. His breath rasped in his ears. Dust showered into his hair, onto his shoulders. The fingers of his left hand, his toes, numbed under the force of holding his body in place. Then a section of bamboo popped free. He knocked it up and back and grappled his way into the stuffy closeness between the bamboo and the thatched roof. A trembling seized him. But he willed himself to be calm. To meticulously settle the loose bamboo back into position. Then he eased himself onto his stomach. He lay rigid, unmoving, as he had during the boyhood games of hiding he and Frank had invented while they were guarding the family herds. Only this was no game. This was . . .

"Traitors!"

The cry split the air, pounding into a hundred bloodthirsty cries. Chinks between the bamboo canes gave him full sight through the open door and into their backyard. Three men pushed around the house. Filthy. Hair matted. Rags, not banana leaves, coiled their heads. One with a club. Another a spear. The third a machete.

His breath froze. *No!* Even through the mud streaking the face and the layers of rags flopping crazily around the sweating body, he would recognize that one anywhere. The throbbing yells. The panic. The day of the helicopter. The distant shrill threat. "They chop off Tutsi heads!" *Haricot!* Richard's head threatened to explode.

They pushed out of view.

KILL THY NEIGHBOR

Splintering wood. Banging. Hollering. Crashing glass. Frenzied oaths. Then new screams ripped the mayhem. Richard's life blocked into a wooden slow motion. Detail followed horrible detail. His machete-wielding classmate. The other two. His mother. Dragged before the open doorway. Pleading for pity. Pleading. Crying out her innocence. Praying.

"Mother!"

His mouth scorched with the silence of the word he dared not vocalize. A frantic impulse pushed him to throw himself down from his hiding place. To stop her attackers. But he lay. Rigid. Eyes wide. Watching what he had no power to stop. It was as though they did not know her. Did not hear her. The machete. The club. The spear.

"My mother!"

Then it was Shema.

Then Robert.

Shock after shock pulsed through his body. His mind numbed. He lapsed into a stupor. Lying as still as the bodies in the scarred courtyard.

After the mob left, even after darkness fell, he still did not move from where he lay. His heart cried, begged, shouted at him to climb down and scrape out a hollow grave for their poor bodies, to give them the dignity of being received by the earth. His good sense, though, held him where he was. Warned him not to move. Not to do anything that might attract attention. Not to leave any sign that he or any of his family might still be alive.

C H A P T E R

26

Charles and the Guards

Night wore itself into day. At midmorning he became aware of a rustling. He peered down and saw two of the younger ones, his littlest sister and a brother, lighting a fire. He started to move, to speak, but a foreboding seized him. Just then, someone rushed in. And grabbed them. And dragged them away.

Another day went by. And night. Malachai also came. Cared for the cows. And left. He returned again when another dusk was dropping over the silent courtyard, shuffling toward the animal shed.

Richard forced himself to climb down.

"Richard?" The stocky Hutu froze, as if seeing someone from the spirit world.

"I need your help." In the back of his head, he could hear his mother's voice, hear her saying, "You can always count on Malachai," and now he counted on their years of living as brothers to cement the fidelity of the Hutu who stood across from him with his own desperate needs.

Malachai regarded him silently. "What should I do?" His low voice sounded as dull as the shadows.

"I have two friends. Members of the president's political party. I'll write a note. Ask them to come and get me."

Malachai waited while Richard went to his room. The door stood open, but everything seemed as it always had been. His grandfather's spear stood harmlessly in the corner. His baton. The stool. The flute of the long-silent melodies that had held at bay the long-ago bandits. He left them as they were and took pen and paper. "I'll pay you well," he promised and signed his name. When he handed the note to Malachai, he asked the question that he dreaded to form. "My father?"

Malachai regarded him from hopelessly bleak eyes.

"What happened?"

"Today. In a banana patch. They found him."

"The same ones?"

"I don't know. Some say it was the FPR. Some of their scouts sneaked in. Because of what happened to your mother. And others."

When Malachai left, Richard went to the house. In a haze of not wanting to believe what he was doing and why, he went to the hiding place where his mother kept the business money. Then he went back to his room. Collected his own savings; collected some clothes, including the blue shirt Shema had washed and the other one; put them in a bag; picked up the photo album; pushed it in with them; and then sank into a chair and waited. It was full night when the motorcycle finally growled up to their gate.

"Climb on." The driver wasted no words. "Between us. We're taking you to the border of the prefecture."

They roared into the night. Toward morning, they reached the last militia barricade. "You can manage from here." The driver nodded his head toward the road on the other side. "The Tanzania border's just there. By morning . . ." His words took for granted that Richard would join one of the many traumatized groups of citizens fleeing the bloodshed that had driven them from their homes.

"Who're you?" a guard demanded, shining a flashlight in Richard's face.

Richard held up his identity card.

The guard looked and grunted. "It's cold, you know." His voice took on a different demeanor. "We need matches."

"Matches, is it?" the driver interjected somewhat cheerfully from where he sat.

"Matches," returned the guard.

"And how much will they be?"

The guard named his price. Richard reached into a pocket that held a portion of his mother's savings and counted out enough francs to light fires for the entire army during the next ten years and laid them on the outstretched hand.

The guard opened the gate and motioned him through. He trudged into the darkness. Behind him, the motorcycle turned and roared off in the direction from which he had just come. Dark patches of cloud blotched out most of the stars. He sensed more than saw the others on the road ahead. By dawn, they came to a crossroads. Clumps of people covered the road. Trudging away from what had happened. Bundles and baskets and rolled mats balanced on their heads. From Byumba. From Ruhengeri. From Kigali.

"Tanzania?" A patriarchal voice formed the question, then hurried on to give its own answer. "No. No. We'll turn toward Gitarama. It'll be like the war of 1990. In a few days, everything will be calm. We'll content ourselves to go to Gitarama, to wait there until we can go home."

Richard looked toward the rising sun. *Tanzania?* his thoughts repeated. Two days earlier, that's where he thought he wanted to go. That was before. Numbly he stared along the fork to his left.

"Do what you need to do to save yourself."

Mother? His thoughts did not want him to remember what had happened. And he stood mutely at the crossroads. One among the scores upon scores of the displaced. Others wandered the roadway. This way. That. Threading in. Between. Separating. Collecting. Bunching. Forming groups. He stood. Alone. Eyes seeing. Mind not able to place himself in either direction. Left? Right?

"It will be like the war of ninety." The grizzled old patriarch spoke again to those who were with him, encouraging them to turn, to walk with him toward Gitarama.

"It will be like the war of ninety." Richard repeated the sentence as if it were just another line given to him to memorize for an examination. "Like the war of ninety." No one rushed behind him in hot pursuit. He heard no threatening voices. He did not have to leave. Abandon his country? His home? Like that? By himself? For no immediate reason? *I'll go to the university.* The rising sun pointed rays of brightness along the highway toward Kigali, the normal route to take for Butare. Groups straggled along the paved surface. Some going. Some coming. Some, he could tell even from a distance, wounded. "The news is good," one of the nearer travelers replied to his greeting. "But in Kigali the fighting is bad. Very bad. Many people have been killed, and bodies are lying in the roads. That is not the way to go for now."

Richard listened. "Bodies. In the road." His mind echoed what he had just been told. "Bodies." His voice echoed when the man had pointed in the direction of Richard's own home. "Many families killed. That is not the way to go for now." But like the others, he said nothing of what he personally had seen or of what had happened to his own family. And then he turned onto the dirt road that cut through the south and toward Butare. A battered green pickup stood by the side of the road.

"Certainly, I'll take passengers," the owner of the pickup agreed. A merchant, also fleeing, he named his price. When they approached the village of Rwabusoro, they found themselves suddenly facing a rude barricade of boards and barrels. Guards rushed over to them, clubs in hand.

"Who are all these you have with you?" The chief shoved his head through the driver's window. His men spread like sentries, picketing the vehicle.

"They're my passengers."

"You're taking all these enemies with you?"

"No need to exaggerate." The driver's voice and jovial vocabulary gave the idea he was engaged in an everyday duel of friendly give-and-take. "I would travel only with those who are loyal to our country."

"Who, then, are those conspirators I see in the back?" A burly fellow in torn jeans and faded shirt pushed up beside his chief, the stained bill of an old baseball cap flopping over one ear. "There!" A jagged scar laced the arm that pointed.

"I have no conspirators aboard, I can assure you." The driver continued to talk calmly. "They are only a few simple men and women who are coming with me to Gitarama."

"Down!" The chief suddenly stepped away from the door and signaled with his club toward those riding in the back.

No one moved.

"I said get down!" He swung his club above his head and advanced.

Several of the women clambered down.

"You! You and you!" On the final *you*, he jabbed his club toward Richard.

Richard hoisted himself over the bundles that were jammed against his legs and slid to the ground. Suddenly, the gang closed around them. Clubs and machetes bristled in their hands. Ragged. Filthy. Most with rags bound around their heads, they prodded their captives to the side of the road. Each eyed the person nearest. "You." A stocky one grasped the arm of the woman huddled by Richard and hauled her out of the group. "Back on the truck."

The woman scrambled nimbly aboard and crouched in the far corner. A few others were shoved in the same direction. Richard stood where he was.

"Let the rest of these back on too," suggested the driver. "I tell you, they're innocent. They're all . . ."

"Traitors!" screamed the chief. "Take your truck and go. We know what to do with these."

Richard's stomach squeezed into the same sort of solid, cold knot he had felt when he had crouched in the attic three days earlier.

"How much?" the driver demanded.

"No price can buy them. They are destroying our country. Now it is their turn to be destroyed."

The chief pushed closer. The others pushed with him. They edged their prisoners off the road and toward . . .

As they pulled to a stop, Richard saw a heap of fresh earth just beyond a gap in the trees. Beside a newly dug pit. In the direction they were being moved. He ground his back molars together, hard, and let his eyelids drop momentarily. *Mother.* The word burned through his mind.

"Richard!"

Everyone started. Richard's head jerked around to look in the direction of the voice.

"What are you doing here? Sha, Richard. It's been a long time, friend."

"Charles!"

"Why've you arrested him?" Charles turned toward the gang's chief. "Release him. He's coming with me." And to Richard he said, "Come. Let's have a drink before you go."

Obediently Richard followed his old school friend.

"Yes," Charles explained, after he had ordered a boy to run to the nearest shop and bring them something to drink. "I've been teaching school here for several years. Good years. Except that with all the events, some of the young fellows you see here tend to get carried away with their ideas." He spoke with a forced cheerfulness, and loudly enough that his authoritativeness would register on those at the barricade. "But you'll see. In a short while, everything will work itself out. Things will settle down. Life will resume its usual calm. Sha, Richard! It is good to see you again."

Richard sipped his drink when it came. Charles ordered more drinks for the guards. "And now about those others." He turned toward the chief.

The chief did not reply.

"Don't you think it's time for me to load my other passengers?" the driver added.

Charles and the driver discussed and pleaded. Finally, they secured the release of two more. With that, the guards turned deaf ears. "Go!" The chief shook his club angrily in the face of the driver. "These Tutsi enemies! They must pay for their crimes! If you don't leave, we'll take you and everyone! Go!"

"You'd better leave," Charles whispered.

The driver took a quiet breath, turned, and climbed back into the cab. When they drove off, everyone kept their eyes down so they would not have to look at those they had left behind.

CHAPTER 27

Butare Again

They reached another fork in the road. Richard and five others climbed down. When the old pickup rattled on its way, they set out on foot in the direction of Butare. By nightfall they had reached a Catholic health center. "We're fugitives," they explained to the nun on duty. "Hutus."

She invited them in. A European sister bustled off in the direction of the kitchen, then returned to call them into the dining room. Richard seated himself at the table, studied the plate that had been set before him, and then looked up into the kindly blue eyes. His throat knotted. "Thank you, Sister," he forced himself to say. "What you have done for us is very kind." The walls of his throat seized together and the muscles behind his eyes stiffened with a hot ache. He tried to form words that would wish her God's blessing, but the words would not come, for his mind was filled with the scenes in his father's courtyard. He touched the spoon beside his plate. Forced himself to pick it up, to ladle some of the soup, but he could not make himself swallow.

Later, the sisters brought them sleeping pads, and he sank

onto one in the waiting room and lay, silent and unmoving, but his eyes did not close in sleep. With morning's first light, they again set out. It was Monday, April 18. Eleven days had passed since the president's death.

By midday they reached a stretch of the inter-African highway, a section on the link that curls west from Kampala in Uganda and then south and across the border into Rwanda, through Byumba and into Kigali, west again the fifty-some kilometers to Gitarama before it turns south toward Butare and the Burundi border. During the night, it had rained, but the gritty shoulders had already dried and lay in dust-gray strips along the black asphalt. The single line of eucalyptus on either side, white-trunked and stately, stood guard as always. Richard faced south toward Butare, toward the direction from which he had come less than two weeks earlier. For a brief instant, he remembered the warmth and lightheartedness that had filled his Peugeot that sunny afternoon and the joy of having Aline beside him and of talking about their wedding plans.

"See you soon!"

Her last words as they said goodbye in front of her sister's house in Kigali rang in his ears.

"Sha, Rich . . . !"

He started, looking quickly to his right. But it was not Aline. It was some other feminine voice calling out to someone named Richli, whom she had seen among the jostle that strung along the roadside, where scattered handfuls of fugitives trudged north while others headed south. His feet moved automatically, lifting, stepping ahead, touching earth momentarily. His companions from the pickup faded into the crowd, and he was left alone. Heaviness settled over him, but he tried to keep himself from thinking, to keep himself from remembering, to keep himself even from endeavoring to reason out where Aline might be.

"Surely she's left Kigali." His thoughts refused to obey and persistently tried to establish her most likely whereabouts. "Maybe she's with her parents. Maybe already in Butare. Maybe she's found a ride. Maybe . . ." The pace of those walking ahead of him slowed.

"Doctor!"

A fatigue-clad figure pushed in front of him, and he realized they'd reached another barricade. The face seemed familiar.

"Remember? You treated my mother at the hospital!"

"Ah yes." Automatically, Richard slipped into the doctor's attitude he'd been taught to assume. "And how is your mother now?"

"Fine. Very fine. Are you on your way back to the university?"

"Yes."

"Then continue on your way."

The soldier's friendliness was like a cup of cool milk to a thirsty traveler, and Richard felt a new confidence. Just past the barricade, he heard someone else calling his name.

"Want a ride?"

A friend sat in his vehicle at the side of the road.

Richard gladly accepted. In Butare city, he found other university friends, most of them Tutsis. "What's the news from Kigali?" they asked. "And in Gitarama? Have you heard anything about . . . ?" They listed names of mutual acquaintances.

Richard could reply only vaguely to their questions. "Really, I don't have any news," he finally said. "I've had the chance to arrive from the north with some others who found it safer to come this direction, but I have no news I can tell you about any of the events." He made no reference to what he himself had experienced. He couldn't.

Others continued to pepper him with questions, anxious to have any word about friends and families in the north and in the east of the country, considering that Richard, having just arrived, could give them firsthand information. But he could tell them nothing. "Then tell me," he finally asked, "how is it at the university? Should I go to the campus?"

"We're staying there, but there's only one meal a day at the cafeteria." His friends explained that the roadblocks had essentially paralyzed the area and that no one could get through with food. "There's nothing at the city markets. But the university has rice in stock. We're trying to negotiate with the administration to feed us with that, and then we'll pay it back when the situation settles so classes can resume."

Rain had begun falling by the time he had decided to hike back to the campus, a solitary part of the crowd of wanderers who, as he had done, had come not knowing where else to shelter. Young folks in scattered knots of three or four or more huddled under overhangs on the campus as they always had on a rainy evening. It was all so the same as always, and yet everything had changed. In the lounge, the TV blared. Only now its commentary matched screens full of bodies, victims massacred on the other side of the country. Radiocasts were equally grim. His Hutu and Tutsi friends no longer mingled. Hutus grouped with Hutus. Tutsis grouped with Tutsis. And between them hovered an invisible barrier. Had he been asked to choose one word to sum up the atmosphere, he would have replied without hesitation: *fear.*

Girls stayed the night with their boyfriends. Even if a boy had talked with a girl only once and she had no one else, he was now, by obligation, her close friend and thus compelled to take her to his room for protection. Other Hutsis had also returned. But they were too few to form their own group. Besides, politics had virtually forced everyone to choose one side or the other. Some chose to identify themselves as pure Hutu. Others chose to be Tutsi. Richard had chosen to support anyone who took a moderate stance, promising to support the cause of rights for everyone, regardless of ethnic origins. He went to his room. Alone. Aline and Sylvie and Lydia and Cyusa had not returned with the others who had come from Kigali. And no one could tell him news of any of them.

The next day, he went back to his usual responsibilities as a senior medical assistant at the student dispensary. Rumors said that the massacres were nearing, that everyone, regardless of tribe, was being slaughtered in an area to their north. During the day, he heard shots and the whooping cries for help. On Wednesday, the vice rector of the university met with the students in the outdoor court. "What about us?" one of the students asked. "If something should happen, will the university assume responsibility?"

"This is war. Those of you who are here . . ."

Just then, Richard saw people running away from the houses on the hillside opposite the sports field where the students sat on the bleachers, toward the campus. Soldiers swept into his line of sight. Firing at those running. Firing at houses. Firing. A rattle of rapid shots sounded nearer. Richard jerked his head in the direction from which they seemed to come. Silence dropped.

"You are considered as all other fugitives who have fled the fighting."

A single shot cracked. Richard felt a small, dark object whine by his cheek. He threw himself onto the cement. Face down. Hands locked behind his head.

"Richard!"

He dared not move.

"Richard!"

He heard voices laughing. Cautiously, he lifted his head, rolled his eyes upward.

"That was a fly!"

Grinning sheepishly, he scrambled back onto the bench. After the meeting, he went back to the student health center. Since the vice rector had decreed that under no circumstances was anyone to leave the campus, he reasoned that the health center would have plenty of business. Just as darkness fell that evening, shooting started again. "The city of Butare was officially attacked at six-fifteen," the radio news reader announced. The news was chilling. "The first person to be killed was Ichanda." Ichanda was the widow of the old Tutsi king, Mwami Mutara III, who had died in mysterious circumstances in a Bujumbura hospital in 1959. A brilliant burst of light flared momentarily, and a dozen quick blazes streaked along the ridge.

Why didn't I go to Tanzania? Back in his room, Richard pulled away from the window and pushed himself against the wall where he could not be seen. *I was there. At the border.* Reflection from another bright blast flashed across the window. *Why?* As the night progressed, several students quietly slipped away. Some locked themselves in unoccupied rooms. Others huddled together in a single room, forming compact groups for protection. Richard chose to stay alone. *If I hide, it's the same as saying I'm an accomplice. If they search and don't find me, they'll wonder why. If I've been seen with x or y or z, they'll find them and ask questions. I don't want to put anyone else in danger. If they find me . . . No. It's best that I stay right where I am.*

God Will Take Care of Us

The flat, scraping sound of hard soles against cement scratched a path from one side of the room and then back to the other. "If they come . . ." Richard's hands burrowed into his pockets, deep, and his head bent forward. "Yiiyiiyiiyii!" The aspirated exclamation only emphasized the solid, impenetrable blank that stood before all his questions. The solid edge of his table suddenly blocked his way. He started to turn. To begin the methodical retracing of his steps. But he paused. Instinctively, he took his hands out of his pockets and reached out with his right hand and let it close around the narrow black photo album, which lay in its usual place. The folded, hard backing, creases along its spine supple from much use, fell open naturally in his hands. His right thumb hooked between a set of the plastic pockets, and he flicked them upward. They fell open to the set of photos he and Aline had taken at the Jacaranda. One of him on the balcony. The other of her, the city hazing out of focus in the distance. He hooked his thumb in again. And again. Flipping through the layered photos, one by one. And then he paused. At the photo of Aline by a church.

"Have you had any news from Aline?"

KILL THY NEIGHBOR

He did not know how many times he had heard that question.

"She'll come." That's what he had said. Repeating the same answer over and over. To all of them. "Imana willing, she'll come."

He himself had repeated the same question. Like everyone else who was missing someone, he kept asking those he met who had been in Kigali when the events broke loose. "Have you any news of Aline?"

No one had seen her. No one could give him a clear answer. No one could tell him a thing of her whereabouts.

"Imana willing."

He looked up. Beside his table, braced into the corner with fronds splaying out gracefully just as he had left them the day before Easter, stood the branches Aline had arranged for him. They were all dry now. Foliage a brittle brown. Dead.

"They're nice," she had said. She was always wanting him to bring in flowers or branches or something from the outside to add life to his room.

"Nice."

"Huh-huh-huh." His throaty chuckle had developed a hollowness, had become brittle like the dry leaves standing in the corner. He went to his bed and let himself flop into a haphazard sprawl. The album dropped beside him. He stared up at the ceiling, his eyes tracing around a large, bulbous water stain.

"She'll come. Imana willing." That's what he promised himself again and again.

Rifle fire crackled in the distance. His eyes remained focused on the ceiling, and he gave no sign of hearing the shooting and the screams. "The will of Imana will be done." That's one of the last things he had ever heard his mother say. "The will of Imana."

A dull chill gradually rose along his back and then seemed to reach around his chest, vicing around him more and more tightly. He felt himself drifting, felt himself back on the ceiling of their kitchen hut, and the cries in the distance hammered together with echoes of the attackers who had forced through their gate.

"Mama!"

The cry forced out between his lips. He squeezed his eyes shut. At that moment, more shots echoed along the ridge toward town. And screams. And then he caught himself and realized that he was in his room at Butare. Alone. Gunfire ripped the night again.

The will of God? This? Evil men destroying the innocent?

The back of his mind replayed something from the hazy distance. "Why should a child have to suffer so?" It was his own boyish voice echoing through a gloomy chamber at the seminary. "Why would it have been in God's plan for a mother to have been separated like that from her children?"

"My son." The answer had belonged to a priest among those who had been kindly disposed toward him during his stay at their school. "The way of suffering is seldom clear. The good Lord has called upon many to bear a heavy cross of sorrow."

If the answer had been intended to bring him comfort, it didn't. And in his mind the Christian God linked even more strongly with the perverse ancestral spirits of his grandfather's beliefs.

Someone knocked. *They've come!* His heart threatened to stop beating. "Yes!" He forced himself up onto an elbow.

The door pushed back haltingly, and then he saw Placide.

"Richard?"

"Come in. Close the door." Richard swung his feet over the edge of his bed and sat up and motioned toward a chair.

"Have you heard the radio?" A chalky pall deadened his friend's dark features.

"You mean the speech?"

"That. And the news. It's finished for us." Placide eased himself onto the chair. "They're as much as saying that all the Tutsis should be killed."

Another blaze of shots in long, repetitive staccatos pounded through the darkness. Placide jerked his head around toward the window.

"Are you going to stay on campus?" Richard noted that the veins in his classmate's eyes stood out much too darkly, making the whites of his eyes mottled like those of one who had drunk too much for too many years.

"Where can we go, Richard? Where can we be safe?"

"I think the safest place is right here. If we run, that's the same as saying we're guilty. If we stay . . ." Richard looked at his Hutsi friend, whose features also favored the Tutsi side of his family. "Even though Butare is falling, the university may still stay neutral. This is the center for our country's intellectuals, the center of its leaders of the future. Our country needs a group who have not been touched by this blood."

"That's what I'm thinking too. You know . . ." Placide stopped himself as if he were about to say something that he did not want to say. "It's almost unbelievable how a few can inflame so many. As if something wicked within the heart of everyone has just been waiting for a key to turn and to let it out. I think . . ."

The two friends chatted, using their conversation to block out the gunfire and the distant screams, as if this was simply another evening when one student exchanged philosophical theory with the other.

"But . . ."

Placide let his voice trail away and stared into some faraway place, as if he, too, were seeing again things that were still too painful to be put into words, even as Richard kept all the real happenings at his home locked away deep within himself. No one on campus spoke of killings witnessed. No one voiced the real reasons that had propelled them to seek safety at the university. To hear them talk, one would have the impression that everyone there had been protected, that none had been touched in real life by the carnage filling the screens of the campus television sets. For a moment, Richard feared his friend might let down his guard and admit to what had happened, to speak of the terrible thing that had caused his flight back to the campus.

"God is with us," Placide finally said. "He'll take care of us."

This sudden deviation caught Richard off guard. "How can you say that?" The tone of his voice did nothing to veil the intensity of his disagreement, though he knew his friend belonged to an active Christian group. "Don't you see what's happening around us?" His face felt stiff, hard. "How can it be that a God of love would be able to allow something of this nature to happen?"

"These are not the doings of God." Placide stared toward the window now, and from where he lay, Richard could see his friend's muted reflection on the glass, chalky sick face against the dull dark green of his shirt. "This can only come from the devil. Like in the case of Job."

"If that is so, then for what good reason does God refuse to do something? Why doesn't He stop this?"

"He is doing something." Placide spoke quietly.

Richard started to interrupt, to argue, then held his words.

"God is doing something," Placide repeated. "Even if it has no appearance that He is. Even if . . ."

Richard could see the muscles in Placide's neck tense, then begin to work up and down as if he suddenly had the need to remove something that had slipped into his throat, blocking it. Finally, he managed to swallow. And to clear his throat.

"Even if we lose everyone and everything," he was saying, and he swallowed again. Hard. "No matter what, I know God is still there. I know He's watching. He's seeing everything. I don't want to die any more than anyone else, but no matter what happens, someday He'll make it right. I know He will."

"I hope so," was all that Richard dared to say.

The boys sat in silence a long while. "Richard." Placide stood and held out his hand. "Friend. May God give you courage. May God give us the courage we need."

Placide left with a step that was more sure and more firm than when he had come, but when he shut the door behind him, Richard flopped back onto his bed, his hands unconsciously smoothing the ripples in the spread that had bunched beside him. He heard the guns firing. "If I escape. If I die." Again his eyes traced the water stain on the ceiling, and his chest felt tight, making it hard for him to breathe normally. "Does it make any difference to God? Whoever He is?"

For the rest of that night, he dared not shut his eyes. Dared not take off his clothes. Dared not take off his shoes. If someone came, he would be ready to go.

CHAPTER 29

May God Help Your Soul

The next morning, as he crossed toward the health center, Richard passed clusters of students standing in silence. Others paced the streets. He greeted those nearest. Just after three that afternoon, as he sat by the center's reception desk, a shadow seemed to fall over him.

"Hssst. Richard."

He looked up.

"Soldiers. Armed to the teeth. They've just taken some students. Christine-Marie, Amoni, Placide . . ."

Placide!

Again another of those cold sensations slapped against Richard's back and washed up and around his chest, and again he felt that tightness that did not want to let him breathe. He struggled against it and forced himself to speak normally. "Is that so?" he heard himself say through the mask that was now his face.

"They searched your room. But they've left just now. With the others in a red pickup."

The informer left.

Who was friend? Who was foe? He had no way of knowing anymore.

The one who had just come might have been trying to help. On the other hand, this might have been a test, a trap to trick him into expressing himself in a way that might prove that he sided with the FPR. Every nerve told him to run. His good sense, though, warned him that there was no longer safety in running; that with Butare ravished, the demonic killing mania now gripped the entire country, and his only safety lay in staying on campus and staying by his post at the health center. As long as he continued treating patients and made himself useful, the killers would not touch him. What he did not know then was that during the morning a government minister had been on campus meeting in secret with selected students, forming them into a squad to work with the military. "Tutsi enemies and their collaborators have escaped justice in the north and in the east and in the west. They are here," he told them. Then he issued his mandate. "Justice to whom justice is due."

A few minutes after six, Richard closed the dispensary door and headed toward the campus cafeteria. The food stock, intended for the last quarter of school, which was to have begun the previous Monday, was now being used to serve the refugee students two meals a day. Birds trilled routine evening melodies. Voices babbled in the distance. He locked the door, then turned and stepped onto the pathway that led along the sports terrain with tennis, handball, and other playing fields toward a normal meal on what to all appearances was a normal April evening. Shouted commands suddenly cut through the gathering dusk. A squad of helmeted, fatigue-clad figures pushed out of the cafeteria entrance. Students, prodded by more soldiers, followed.

"Line up! Line up!"

Hasty, semistraight lines began to form. Richard hesitated, started to turn.

"You! Over here!"

Richard's body tensed, ready to run.

"Be quick! In line."

Bayoneted rifles bristled over shoulders of the soldiers. Knives decorated belts. Rounds of ammunition draped chests. Richard's legs became mechanical walking pieces that responded to the order and took him in the direction the soldier indicated. He had no choice but to let himself be shoved in among his campus comrades. Hutus, Tutsis, Hutsis, all were there. No one spoke, except for the soldiers who had begun plodding methodically along the lines. They were joined by a band of students who swaggered with them like self-important military aides. No one escaped their dark, piercing glares. Richard kept his own eyes lowered, yet he regarded them discreetly. All were Hutus, known political extremists. His heart caught. *Laurence. Him too!*

"Enemy of the republic!"

The charge lanced through the quickly deepening dusk. Immediately, a bayoneted gun swung toward the one singled out, shuffling him to the side like some unwanted insect that had dropped into a plate of soup. Richard's heart threatened to knot into itself. This was not like his arrest in Kigali. This was a hundred hells worse. He watched the soldiers following their aides, taking their time along the lines, culling out the ones they did not want.

They neared.

"Him!"

A student, a fugitive from a Kigali campus, jabbed his hand toward Richard.

"He's one of *them! Inkotanyi!*"

The last word spat toward Richard, and legs numb and unfeeling, he let himself be prodded with the gun, out of line and to the side. *Inkotanyi!* His mind seized around that epithet, which with recent events had been turned against anyone accused of siding with the FPR, and he felt himself being pushed toward the huddle ringed by bayoneted guns in full light from the cafeteria windows. Then they were being herded like senseless pigs toward the road.

"Richard!"

Through a haze, he heard the voice calling his name.

"Richard! Take thirty thousand!"

His hand obligingly pushed into his pocket. It clamped onto a wad of francs. Thirty thousand. For some reason, which his benumbed mind could not comprehend, he knew he had thirty thousand. He pulled it from his pocket. He felt a knife point jab against his neck. A soldier grabbed out, stripped the money from his hand.

"Leave the boy!"

The knife was pulled away from him.

"We'll see about him later."

Somehow he was pushed into the shadows, against a row of bushes. He forced his aching eyes to look away from the soldiers and their guns. Away from the bayonets and knives. Away from the ones being marched toward the waiting red pickup. He let his feet carry him along the shadows and onto a deserted pathway. Suddenly, he sensed someone behind him.

"Richard."

He froze.

"Richard." The person pushed around him and turned, blocking him in a shadowy light.

"Laurence?" He started to throw up his hands to defend himself. "Please . . . no . . . I . . ."

Richard let his hands fall.

"We've grown up together. We've lived together."

Richard stared into the heavy-jowled face of his old school chum, one of his and Frank's teammates in their pickup games of street soccer, a boy from a cultivator's family who lived in a lopsided old hut on the fringes of the commune. In his worst nightmares as a child, he could never have imagined a day when he would stand before Laurence unable to speak or to move, knowing that just a word from the boy's thick lips could send him to immediate death.

"Richard, friend. They have you on their list. They accuse you of having been named as the minster for social affairs in the government the FPR expects to create. There was nothing I could do. Nothing. Even if I hide you in my room . . . Richard, if someone finds you there, we'll die together. There's no pity left. Aaahhh. Friend. Aaaahhh."

The agony in Laurence's voice began to register, cutting through the numbness that blocked his mind. Only minutes earlier, he had dared to let himself hope that his money had bought his freedom.

KILL THY NEIGHBOR

That the night would pass and that he would be spared. But now he understood. That was only a tactic. A delaying strategy used to place his money in the pockets of the ones to whom it had been promised. He had been saved from one march, but others were coming.

"The only help I can give you is to tell you that whatever you do, don't hide." Laurence was still talking. "Sha, Richard, you're a marked man. Stay with the others," he was saying. "And maybe . . . aaaaahhhh." Again that agonized half groan. "I have come to tell you adieu."

Richard became aware of a light touch on both of his arms that was the gentle embrace of their people.

"Adieu, Richard. My friend. May God help your soul." With that, Laurence turned and strode toward the campus square.

For a long while, Richard stood motionless, staring into the night. Going back to his room was now out of the question. Hiding was impossible. He finally obliged his feet to move one after the other in the general direction of the square. He dared not stop to speak with anyone. *They* were watching. *They* would mark anyone to whom he spoke as an accomplice, a traitor, an enemy of the country. *They*. He did not know all those included in the *they*, but he had seen some at work by the cafeteria, and he knew that others of the same sort lingered in the shadows.

Aaaahhh, Richard, his own agonized voice echoed despairing tones in his thoughts. *Aaaahhh, Aline.* For a moment, he held the memory of her gentle face, the memory of her soft voice, the memory of her quiet kiss, the memory of her last words. "Good luck!" If ever he needed good luck! If ever he needed a miracle more than good luck! "See you soon!" He looked up into the heavens and wondered if he would ever live to see her again. And then he allowed himself a long, wistful hope, a somehow prayer to the supreme being that this horror would pass and that soon they would stand together as husband and wife.

C H A P T E R

30

Modeste

Another group of students strode toward the square. Behind them marched more soldiers, guns in hand, bayonets glinting oddly, reflecting the glare of the streetlights. Richard saw them push into a residence hall. Minutes later, the students reappeared. Alone. Then they cut across the square to stop near him.

"That one next."

One of the boys held a list, and Richard saw him pointing toward a residence hall. Richard edged nearer. Before the full impact of what he was doing could register in his own mind, he edged nearer yet and then by some unknown power felt a sudden fearlessness, as if this were just any other warm and normal evening on their quiet campus and as if he were making his way toward a group of students to join in their discussion of some casual campus topic. "*Ach! Tien!*" The French expression of friendly surprise sprang from his lips, sounding as though he had seen something that had been contrived as a joke on someone. "I see my name there! Among those who are being searched!" He pointed toward the paper the group leader held. "Now, how could that be? Who could have done such a thing?"

193

13—K.T.N.

KILL THY NEIGHBOR

"*Ach! Tien!*" the leader echoed. He swept Richard with a glance that registered first confusion and then surprise. "Is it true? Is it you? Is it really you?" His questions rattled out with faked shock, implying that he had no idea that the list he held could possibly contain the name of the one now confronting him.

"I'm astonished that you should put me on the list." As he spoke, Richard was even more astonished at his own courage and tenacity. Even then he realized that the words he was using and the freedom with which he was speaking could only be coming from some power other than himself. "A minister in the FPR cabinet! I'm astonished!" he repeated. "How could anyone dare accuse me of that?" He feigned impatience. "But since I'm here, instead of making you waste your time going to my room and breaking down the door, I'll just wait with you, and if you need me, you won't have the inconvenience of having to hunt for me."

"Who's put his name on the list?" The leader glared around the circle of his cohorts.

"I don't know," a stocky undergraduate muttered. "Someone must be jealous."

"Or trying to settle some old score," another suggested.

"I say it was . . ." The name suggested was lost in the sudden squabbling that broke out among the group.

Richard stood his ground while they argued, throwing out one idea after another. *A game of coverup*, he warned himself. *For reasons of their own personal safety, they don't want me to know who made the list.*

"Come with us!" The squad chief at last swung a grubby hand in Richard's direction. "We'll see."

Richard trudged after them, into the residence building and along the hall. They approached a door. An overfed member of the squad swung back his foot, then threw it forward against the door's center section. Solidly. Again and again.

Athanase! Nausea twisted up and around, contorting Richard's stomach. *They're taking Athanase! He'll see me!* A hot, searing sensation flushed inside his skull. *He'll think . . .* Richard's mouth went dry, and he ducked his head. *Oh! My God! No!* His breath caught in the back of his throat, and his lungs heaved in shallow, dry spasms. *Laurence warned me. He had the courage to say goodbye. And I . . .* After dragging Athanase from the room, the band moved on.

Head down, Richard tagged after the others. He dared not speak. He dared not leave. Whether it was hours or only minutes later, he had no idea, but finally they turned with their captives toward the kiosk, and when they had almost reached the red pickup, another squad met them. Like some object in a game of sport, Richard found himself being forced away from the first group and drawn into the second.

"Traitor!" A sneer curled the end of the word into a snarl. "Inkotanyi accomplice!" The squad chief's gloating jeers hammered after him as he was propelled back toward the campus and into another residence hall, where he was thrust into the next group to be marched away, and his feet became heavy with the realization that this time there would be no rescue. Out of the building. Down the walk. Along the road. Toward the kiosk. And into the back of the horrible red pickup. Soldiers crowded in, forcing him and the others to the floor. The pickup, listing under the weight of so many bodies, crept toward the highway. "Aline!" Her name echoed in some hollow distance as he was hauled onto the highway and toward the Rwasave valley along the same route his own car had taken them on that carefree day only three weeks earlier. The pickup braked, swung to the right, and bounced onto a dirt track past the garden project and into a secluded corner of the experimental forest, the very forest where he and she had enjoyed so many happy walks and had talked of the rosy future that would be theirs. Now his stomach bunched convulsively. His arms felt numb. A dull, revolving cloud hazed across his eyes. His hands tingled. A hot ache seared over his brain.

"Have pity!" he begged. "I'm innocent! I'm not a traitor! I'm not who you think I am!" His voice became lost in the cries of all the others who were wedged into the crowded vehicle.

They jerked to a halt. The soldiers shoved them down and around, into the glare of searchlights. The piercing beams cut the night, pointing out a crude pit that lay like an open wound gouged between the trees, and the words that had burned from his throat when they were still in the pickup now disappeared into a hard, desperate calm. Every nerve alert, he cast his eyes this way and that, looking for his moment, for a way to fight himself free.

"I'm innocent!" he yelled toward the nearest soldier. "Believe me!" He found his face almost touching the bayonet of the gun in the man's hands. Just beyond, the lights flooded a girl's face, her eyes wide and staring in wordless horror. He could see the sweat on her forehead. "I'm innocent!" he shouted past the bayonet. "If you want proof, ask Nonje!" His words lanced out, cold, powerful. "My cousin! He's a military man! Like you! Ask him! He'll tell you!" Words. His only weapons. He kept throwing them. Again and again. "Ask Nonje! My cousin! He'll tell you! Nonje!"

"Nonje?" a voice hollered past his ear just as someone pushed between him and the gun. "Nonje of . . ."

He heard the name of Nonje's commune.

"Yeah. That Nonje." His lungs gulped for air.

"You're Richard."

"Yeah. I'm Richard."

"Stay by me!"

Gunshots exploded to his left. He felt himself being pushed back. Back. Away from the pit.

"And that one!"

"No!" The soldier jumped in front of Richard, shoving against him, sheltering his body.

"Out of the way!"

The soldier spun around, gun leveled. "No! I know this one!"

"What? You're shielding an Inkotanyi traitor!"

"This one's not a traitor! I know him!"

More shots. And then all was quiet except for the rustling as the squad searched pockets for money and bickered among themselves.

"Stay with me. Don't leave my side." The soldier grasped Richard's arm and guided him back to the vehicle and helped him aboard. "I'm Modeste, Nonje's friend. I came with him one day to visit you on campus, but you weren't in." Modeste continued talking nonstop as they drove back toward the university, as if he did not want to give

Richard a chance to respond.

"Eh? What's he doing back here?" The squad chief jerked his head toward Richard when the pickup pulled in to its waiting place back at the campus kiosk.

"I know this one." Modeste jumped to his feet, gun leveled. "He's no traitor; he's my friend."

"Traitor!" the chief screamed.

"You touch him, I shoot!" Modeste braced himself and settled his finger against the trigger.

"He's a traitor!" the chief screamed again.

"Everyone's at risk of being a traitor. No one touches my friend. Do you understand?"

The chief glowered at Modeste and then stepped to the side. The soldiers jumped down and trudged back toward campus. Richard stayed beside Modeste.

31

Just Keep Walking

Sunrise caught against a cloud bank hovering over the city, momentarily staining it a soft crimson before it grew into the golden promise of a new day. Richard still trudged beside Modeste and woodenly matched his pace. During the long, horrible hours of the night, his body and his person seemed to have evolved into two separate, independent identities, though both moved together through space and toward the central campus square. His cheeks felt pasted to his cheekbones. His throat and chest felt raw. His eyes scratched in their sockets. They saw, yet he did not want them to register what they were seeing. He did not want them to accept the sunrise. Nor did he want them to record the light of the new day. That would end the night. That would make it real.

"We have to stay in the open!" Modeste's voice broke through their silence.

I know that! his mind wanted him to scream. If he did not stay in the open, *they* would come. *They* would say that he was hiding. That he was hiding because he was guilty. And they would take him. Again. "Yeah," he finally replied.

"We're friends. Remember. I'm Nonje's friend."

"Yeah."

Modeste kept talking. "I'm going to stay with you today. We're going to stay together. Here on campus. Where everyone can see us. We're going to talk. We're going to pretend that everything's OK. No one will bother you. You'll see. As long as I'm with you, no one will bother you."

They walked along the road toward the kiosk. The red pickup was nowhere to be seen, and in a detached corner of his mind, Richard tried to tell himself that it had never existed and that the turn after turn when he had ridden with Modeste, first to one wooded area with its crude pit, and then to another—that none of that had ever happened. That the ones who had ridden with them. The ones who . . . His mind went blank. He did not want to remember. He couldn't. And so he continued, one of two young men, the one in mud-stained and rumpled campus casuals, the other in military fatigues, who took the looping longer path back toward the central buildings. They crossed the student square and wandered the streets, the buildings hovering above them, gray and silent. They saw other groups of three or four. Walking. But, like them, none of the others seemed to be going anywhere. They simply walked.

"Just keep walking with me," Modeste was saying. "You're going to be OK. We're all going to be OK. Soon the army will launch a strong offensive, we'll drive back the FPR, we'll settle the government back in Kigali, and everything will be OK."

"Yeah." Richard again replied mechanically, but his mind seemed to be objecting, seemed to be saying that life could never be the same, that too many were gone, that the stains of all their blood had blurred across their country. That none of them would ever forget. But his thoughts formed into no real words, at least not into any he dared say. Despite that, he chatted, saying words that seemed to belong to some other person, words that had no real meaning and no connection with the eternal movement of his feet along first one path and then another.

The sun rose to midday, and then it was sliding into the afternoon sky, and still they walked. This way. That. Tracing the perimeters normally traced by those who lived on campus, following the paths he had walked with Amoni. With Athanase. With Placide. With . . .

KILL THY NEIGHBOR

The names burned in his mind. Burned. And he wanted to pull them out and throw them down and make the ones they represented be there with him. Alive. But he couldn't. They were . . .

A quiet, a hollow and barren void, jarred down around him with every one of his numb and mechanical steps. A terrible quiet. Empty. Just yesterday. They were friends. Classmates. Was it true? Would he never see them again? Impossible. The sun, the birds, the flowers, the buildings. There. As always. As if this were merely another day. A day like any other. As if nothing had happened.

"Soon this will be finished," Modeste was saying, but his words echoed off into a meaningless distance. And later. "My post commander will take you . . ."

Richard heard, and he didn't hear. "Where?" he was asking, but Modeste's answer did not register. Their wandering now swung them again toward the road, and a jeep came, and Modeste told him to climb in. And he did. And the one driving wound them through the streets. And it didn't seem like the city anymore. Not the city with the Jacaranda and the happy times and Aline and Sylvie and Cyusa. Laughing. And he saw them. Some. Too many. Lying along the street. Unmoving. Still. And he didn't want to look. Didn't want to see them. Didn't want to remember. But they were there. And he couldn't help seeing them. Men. Women. Grotesque. Children. They cut around to the far side of town. Turned along more streets. Stopped. In the drive of a big house. Almost a villa. "A Tutsi home." He heard the adjutant's distant voice saying the words that were supposed to mean something. But for him they were only words. They had no meaning.

The gate grated open, haltingly, bit by bit, and a boy in a sleeveless navy pullover looked out. A Hutu—that was easy to see. The adjutant motioned. "You can stay here," he was saying to Richard. "He's going to stay here," he said to the boy.

The boy said nothing.

The adjutant reached toward his rifle. "And you will say nothing about our visitor."

"No, sir!" The voice lacked enthusiasm. The adjutant seemed as though he was going to take his rifle, as though he intended to use it, but then he left it where it was.

"A Tutsi home. You'll be safe here." Modeste spoke now. "The boy is alone. Their gardener. The family is—uh," he hesitated and then said, "all gone."

"I'll be safe." Richard mechanically echoed the idea. And he realized that they expected him to get down. To leave the jeep. To leave the safety of being in their presence. To go with the boy.

"Come," the boy said, motioning.

With feet instinctively obeying, Richard followed him into the yard. He heard the jeep drive away. He looked at the boy and then up at the big, silent house. "I need help." Those were the first words he could think of to say. "The other students want to kill me. I need you to hide me."

"You can hide here," the boy said. "The house is empty. They took everyone. And . . ." He turned wide, dull eyes toward Richard. "Everyone," he repeated. "With guns and bayonets. There." He pointed toward the front yard.

Richard swallowed. "Can you save me?"

The boy nodded and again motioned for him to follow and led him around the house, to the back, through a door and into a side room. A ladder leaned against the wall. "Up there." He pointed toward the ceiling, and Richard noticed the vague outlines of a trapdoor. "You'll be safe. I am here. Watching." He paused, then offered hesitatingly, "Is there anything you need?"

"I don't know." Richard spoke truthfully. He didn't know what he needed. He didn't know what he wanted.

"If you need me, knock like this." The boy tapped on the wall. *Tap-tap. Tap. Tap-tap.* "I'll look. If there's no one, I'll knock back. Then you can come out. You'll be safe." And he smiled a thin smile, as if he had the hope that his suddenly emptied life might again have purpose. "I am their gardener," he said. And Richard knew he could trust the boy.

He dragged himself up the ladder. The darkness yawned back of the trapdoor, a cavern, a hot, fetid cavern of darkness. Grasping out, he caught hold of a rough crosspiece and pulled himself up and into the dusty heat.

KILL THY NEIGHBOR

He leaned himself against the crosspiece and tried to decipher the context of this new hiding place. But it sprawled into a dim, musky, meaningless space, and he saw only the shadowy crisscrossing of raw rafters and board crosspieces and the straggling remains of a sorghum harvest—some dry leaves and some carelessly scattered round grains. And nothing more. He sank down onto a naked brace and let his head drop into his hands. And sat. Staring down. Seeing nothing. Thinking nothing. Hardly aware of the stifling heat that radiated down from the bare metal roofing, dulled into a flat, unrelenting heating element by the afternoon sun.

The dimness began to fade, and he realized that night was coming. Then he heard it. A scuffled movement. He froze, his body tensing into an unbreathing shadow against the rafters. He heard it again. Like a pant cuff brushing against a dry sorghum leaf. In the far corner. *They've come! They've found a secret entry.* His heart began to heave against his chest. He felt the blood pounding in his ears. He clamped his arm tighter against the rough upright. *The Interahamwe! They've found me!*

CHAPTER 32

In the Attic

The sound. Again. Of someone creeping his way. Richard stared. Eyes wide and scorching dry holes into the darkness. Toward the one who was hunting him. But he saw nothing. Absolutely nothing. *They're coming! They know I'm here!* He cast his eyes about, searching for escape. But darkness was everywhere. Everywhere. Too much darkness.

Then. A scraping leaf.

His chest seized. He tensed. Ready to spring. To fight.

A scampering. A shrill squeak. A series of squeaks. And a scurry of miniature footsteps.

His breath released with a *whoosh*. His body slumped against the upright. "Mice!"

When his terror had passed, he forced himself to get up. A trembling still rose along his legs. He forced them to cooperate, to move his feet ahead, to search the way along the rough cross board, to take a few careful steps. He had to lie down. To rest. To recover his senses. There was a wide spot, an empty spot, toward the slope of the roof. He'd seen it earlier. Had chosen it as his bed. He pushed himself in that direction now. Found it. And curled himself on the unplaned flooring and stared into the blackness. Under better circumstances, the rife atmosphere would have nauseated him. But now it was merely there. Around him. A part of the strangeness, the alien pattern that life had assumed. Voices drifted in from some strange distance. Shouting voices. Then shots. His head snapped upright, neck muscles taught. His ears strained. More shots. Running footsteps.

They're coming! Hide!

No! You are hiding! You're safe! His better self argued against his brute panic. *Nobody knows you're here.*

What if they saw?

They didn't see. Modeste said . . .

The shots. The footsteps. The shouting voices. And then everything faded. Everything. Until it all belonged to a distant blackness. And he let his head drop down and be cradled on his arms. The blackness. The immense wall of blackness. Suffocating, hateful, bloody blackness. Full of enemies and vengeful mobs. Blocking him in, incarcerating him, making it inconceivable for him to walk out and to live and to breathe and move about like a normal human being.

Why didn't you go to Tanzania? When you were there, why didn't you go? Why did you come this way? Why? Why? He twisted on the rough boards, tossing his head side to side. Trying to escape, to get away from the hounding of his own mind. To get away from the fetid, overpowering blackness. To get away. *Why here? Why this direction? Why?* Time became an agony of empty whys and tossing and turning and tortured flashbacks with bayonets and knives and more screams.

With the settling of night, the temperature dropped rapidly, draining away the stuffy daytime heat, and soon he realized that he was cold. Too cold. Hours rolled into one another. Into day, when it again became too hot, and then into night and the cold and then back again into day. The boy came when he tapped. Richard gave him money, and the boy brought him food. And even though his appetite refused the thought of eating, he made himself have something. And then it was night again. Every strange sound. Every unexpected movement. His body tensed. Every time. His heart pounded. His temples throbbed. He broke into a cold sweat. *How long? How long will I have to stay like this?*

Again he began to roll from side to side, his head clamped between his hands, his back arching, twisting. A new wave of nausea rushed over him, flushing through his stomach, washing around his head. He squeezed his eyelids tight, and stabbing red-hot flashes surged through the sockets behind his eyes. *I've got to get away.* His head thrashed. This side. That. Frantically. And again he clamped his hands against it, to calm himself, to make himself be quiet so no one would hear and know that he was there. He dug his fingertips against his scalp as if trying for a pressure point, bearing down, trying to stop the turmoil. His little finger slipped and scraped through the cold, sticky sweat layering his forehead.

"God! My God! Help!"

Round and round and round, words and sentences and vivid flashes of guns and machetes. Spinning. Savage. Sometimes together, sometimes splintering. *God!* His mouth opened wide, forming the word, but he made no sound. *God!* If only he could get ahold of himself. Stop his thoughts. *God!* The word was a prayer. A heart-wrenching prayer. Directed to the supreme, all-powerful One without naming any intermediary. Pleading. Pitiful. *Help! Help me to escape!*

Toward dawn, he began to settle. A name came to his mind. *Gaspard. Officer Gaspard.* And a plan. When full light came, he slipped down the ladder and tapped on the wall, and when he heard the answering tap, he unbolted the door, and the boy came in.

"I need you to help me," Richard said.

The boy nodded.

"I want you to take a message to Officer Gaspard at the military camp. He knows me. He's my neighbor from home."

The boy found a scrap of paper and a pen and brought them, and Richard wrote the message the boy was to take. "I need you." Just those three words and his signature. "If he asks you where I am, tell him that I'm at your place."

The boy left, and Richard climbed back into the attic. *God,* his thoughts milled. *God, let him come. Let him come before the others find me. Let him come before they kill me.*

The morning dragged by. Finally, he heard voices.

"Where is he?" someone demanded.

Richard froze.

"Here!" It sounded like the boy.

Richard began to tremble again. *It's a trap!* he warned himself.

"I want to see him," the voice said.

Richard waited. Heart pounding. Not daring to move. Hardly daring to breathe. Then he heard it. *Tap-tap. Tap. Tap-tap.*

Slowly, quietly, he slipped down the ladder, slid his socked feet silently across the floor, and stood by the door. He could hear them talking now. Plainly. The second voice sounded like Gaspard's. But had he come as a friend? He stared at the door, heart pounding. Then he lifted his hand. *Tap-tap. Tap. Tap-tap.* He waited. When he heard the answering tap, he slid back the bolt, opened the door a crack, then stood back in the shadows away from view.

Then Gaspard entered. They embraced. Spoke the words of greeting that must be spoken. And went to sit on the chairs of the people who were no longer there. Richard faced the officer, still not sure that the man had come in peace. "I need help," he said quietly.

"What is it that you want me to do for you?"

"I need to leave the country."

The officer regarded him silently. "The border is blocked into Burundi," he finally said. "Maybe via Gikongoro and Cyangugu. For us, that way should still be open."

"Then you can help?" Richard tried not to sound too hopeful. "I have money." That was true. He still had the dollars he had saved for his wedding. And some francs he'd taken from the house. Stuffed inside his clothing.

"I'll send some men for you tomorrow. They'll get you past the roadblocks, no problem. Sha, Richard."

The *sha* startled Richard. Gaspard had taken classes with him on campus; they had met occasionally for drinks. But that was years ago. Even centuries.

"You don't have to worry, my friend. You can trust my men."

With Gaspard's confident attitude and his easy willingness to help,

Richard felt his first glimmer of real hope. "Tomorrow," he said. And then the two of them slipped into conversation that belonged between the old classmates and one-time neighbors that they were.

"Do you know a girl by the name of Christine-Marie?"

Gaspard's question caught Richard off guard. "Christine-Marie?" he repeated, and in his own ears he heard that his voice had tensed. *A test?* his mind warned. *Maybe he wants to see how much I know, to see if I know she was in the first group to be taken away.* Aloud he said, "Yes. I know a girl with that name."

Gaspard smiled. "Seems one of our corporals took pity on her. Brought her back to the camp. Says she's his wife."

"Really?" Richard dared not show too much interest.

"Mmm-huh." Gaspard fell silent for a moment, and Richard could see deep shadows around the officer's eyes. "These last days . . ." he began again. "Terrible. We had orders to keep Butare calm. I thought . . . Ach, my friend. Here. Where Hutus and Tutsis have lived in peace for generations." The Hutu officer's shoulders seemed to sag, and he braced his jaw on his fist. "Then that speech by the interim president. Ach, Richard, I don't know if you heard, but the phrases that came from that man's mouth saying that once he had been moderate, but now he'd changed. Like Pilate, that one. His clever rhetoric as much as offering up the innocent as sacrifices. Sacrifices!" He gave his head a quick shake. "And then the visit to campus by the government minister. Gasoline, that. Like throwing fuel onto an already-raging fire. Ach, my friend."

Richard heard the agony. Heard the despair. Heard the voice of a moderate whose dreams for the future had disappeared into worse than nothing.

"When we're finished with this war . . ."

Richard met his friend's eyes now.

"We're going to need the ones like you."

The Church

The next afternoon, Richard sat in the back of a jeep. The driver and his buddy, both wearing full battle dress, had their guns handy. Gaspard's promise the day before to help Richard escape the country had come like a miracle, like an answer to his frantic prayers of the night before. Gaspard had even driven out to the campus and had gone to Richard's room and had found the hidden handbag that contained all his school documents and other important personal papers. Now, dressed in his favorite blue jeans and matching jacket and wearing his best shoes, clothes that Gaspard had also collected for him from the room, Richard assumed the best-possible semblance of nonchalance and noninterest as the jeep rattled up to a roadblock near Gikongoro.

"What enemy do you have there?" The Interahamwe guard stared past the two military men and pointed at Richard. "Just leave him here. Then you can pass."

"We have orders to take him with us."

"What? That traitor?"

"Look at his card. He's Hutu."

"Look at him!" A burly fellow, several grenades stuffed into his belt, jerked his head toward Richard. "Now if you ask me, he looks Tutsi."

"He's Hutu, and we have orders to take him to Cyangugu."

"Orders?" Hoarse laughter met the driver's argument. "Whose orders are those?

"The commanding officer's."

"Commander?" More hoarse laughter. "Tell your commander that this is our barricade, and we say no Tutsis pass. Now, hand him over, and you can go on about your military business."

The soldiers refused.

"All right!" The one speaking hooked a fist toward them. "You won't listen to reason. Then all of you, down." The doors were jerked open, and Richard found himself being pulled out and made to stand at the side of the road beside the two soldiers Gaspard had sent as his escorts. Guns leveled in their direction. "Disarm them."

Two stocky Hutus shoved forward and grabbed for the soldiers' guns. Richard's eyes stared ahead, past them, along a rough dirt trail that wound behind some trees. Two shovels leaned against a mound of earth.

"This needn't be gone about in such a hasty way," one of the soldiers began. "I'm sure we can talk this over and arrive at a mutually agreeable understanding."

"We gave you our terms. No Tutsis."

"We don't have any Tutsis."

"Since you are not willing to cooperate, then we can only arrive at one conclusion. You are all accomplices."

"Now, how can you say that when you see that we have orders from our commander . . ."

The soldiers seemed to be getting the gang leader's attention. They began to negotiate. Richard stood to the side. Finally, a price was agreed on. "But only if you turn around and take this enemy back to Butare."

Richard had pulled a wad of francs from his pocket and had begun counting.

"Match money!" A voice behind his shoulder rolled into a sneer.

Richard continued counting and then handed over the agreed-on price, the equivalent of over $450. The guard in charge motioned them into

209

the jeep, and they turned and headed back toward Butare. A short time later, he sat in Gaspard's military office, and for the first time since he had left his home, he began to talk about what had really happened. He told everything. Not just about this latest problem of being accused of being Tutsi and being prevented from going beyond the barricade, but about his parents, about the night at the university, about Modeste and how he had saved him and had arranged for him to be brought to the Tutsi house. "I've got to leave the country." His voice caught then, and with eyes dry and aching, he looked up at his Hutu friend. "That's the only thing that is left for me to do."

"Tomorrow." Gaspard said the one word as a promise. "I'll drive you myself. The Interahamwe in Cyangugu direction have obviously become too nervous to respect anyone anymore, so we'll go via Gitarama and then across to Gisenyi."

The next afternoon, late, Gaspard came in his jeep with five heavily armed bodyguards. They stopped to spend the night in Gitarama.

"Richard!"

"Antoine!" Richard swung around in surprise when he heard his classmate's voice. "I didn't expect to see you here."

"Yes, my family came from Kigali as soon as we could," Antoine was saying. "It's more comfortable to be near the government and the military."

"I went to the university," Richard said. "And I found that I was deceived in thinking the problems would not touch the campus or any who sheltered there."

"Our entire country has been deceived."

"But when this is over . . ."

Antoine interrupted Richard at that point, but he did not meet his eyes as he asked, "You've had news of Aline?"

"Not yet."

"Oh, Richard, my friend."

"You've seen her?"

"I saw her."

Richard did not reply.

"She was with the group who took shelter in the big Catholic church north of Kigali."

"You're sure?"

"I wish I could say that this was something that I did not know for certain."

Richard remembered nothing more of what was said, nor did he remember going back to the room, nor did he know what he had said when Gaspard had urged him to eat. He did not even know if he had slept during the night. He had become nothing more than a shell that talked and acted on the outside but whose real self had no reality.

The church.

Always before in times of trouble, people had run to their churches. And always before, they had found safety within their walls. But things were no longer like they used to be. Now . . . The Cathedral Nyundo, the large Catholic church at Kebeko, the big Adventist church at Mugonero, another big Protestant church at Kiziguru, the Catholic church at Musha. Other churches. Many others. Catholic and Protestant. People had fled there like hunted animals. And had found the sacred walls useless against the maddened attackers. Grenades and guns. Bayonets and machetes. Clubs and hoes and spears and knives. Gasoline and fire. The devilish work had assumed too many horrible forms, but the results were all the same. No one escaped.

"Good luck!" In some terrible distance, he heard Aline's laughing voice, heard her calling out to him as he drove away on the evening before Easter. "See you soon."

"Aline!" Her name choked in his throat. She, too, was gone. Gone. A gasoline-soaked fire had devoured the church where she and her family had turned for shelter. The very church where she had often prayed and worshiped. Where she had told him to go and find God. *Fire.* Tears burned behind his glazed and aching eyes, but they did not come. The church had not been able to save her.

In the morning, he stumbled out to the jeep. A man without family. A man without a future. A man alone. Terribly and completely alone.

34

The Last Barricade

Gaspard's jeep carried them up and over the Nile Crest. His rank and Richard's money got them past checkpoint after checkpoint. About midmorning, they reached Gisenyi and then pulled up at the final barricade. Several Interahamwe lolled nearby. Gaspard asked for the chief and disappeared into a building. Richard waited in the shade. Minutes slipped into hours. He stared mutely at the ground, but the gritty tan surface tended to waver under his gaze and disappear into churches. Burning churches. In the distance, he heard voices.

"Aline?"

Worn shoes moved into the periphery of his vision.

"Nice jacket!"

The words floated in from overhead now. He looked up. His eyes focused on a gun. It jabbed in his direction.

"Nice jacket, I said!" The grinning mouth that spoke those words framed a set of large, wide-spaced protruding teeth. "I need it."

Richard saw the gun stab again in his direction. He stared at it. At the boy.

"I repeat, I need it."

Richard saw others. Bands of bullets hugged shirts. Grenades poked above belts. Rifles seemed to be everywhere. The message registered, and he shucked his shoulder and slid one arm out of the warm denim. "Looks good on you." Aline's voice came to him from some dimness his mind did not want him to think about. "Wear it." He had worn it. Only now he was silently sliding his other arm out of the other sleeve. It was a good jacket for traveling, for wearing to where he was going, but that was no longer important. Submissively, he took it off and held it out.

The boy snatched it from his hands.

That didn't matter. He still had on his red sweater. And jeans. And again he seemed to find something of interest on the ground in the dust where the feet surrounding him shuffled in and out, arranging and rearranging themselves. Voices continued to float back and forth over him. Beyond them, he could hear other voices locked in tight discussion. "Gaspard?"

The ground by his feet jarred. Another rifle. Pounding.

"Give me my shoes!"

Richard looked at his feet.

"My shoes! Do you hear?"

He bent forward, and his fingers reached toward the laces, moving as if they were appendages that belonged to someone else. They tugged at the laces. First on one. Then on the other. He slipped his feet free and set them down on the ground beside the shoes. And felt the warmth from the sandy soil ease through the thinness of his socks. His shoes stayed where they were, two brown oblongs. Arms reached toward them, and Richard saw that the rifle was now dangling on a strap that drooped from the boy's shoulder. Then he saw the boy straighten and run his free hand over the shoes' polished leather surface. "Nice," he said.

Nice, Richard's thoughts repeated.

To the accompaniment of a slight dip of his head, the boy stuffed the shoes into a worn bag slung at his waist, while, like a weary traveler resting his feet, Richard sat immobile where he was, looking the part of who he was—a university student in red sweater and blue jeans on his way to some destination known neither to himself nor to those who stood around him.

"You!"

Richard's head jerked up at the suddenness of the order. The guard in charge was pointing toward him.

"You! Go!"

Richard jumped up. Then hesitated. "Gaspard?" he wanted to ask. He looked toward the office building. His friend was nowhere in sight.

The guard flicked his hand impatiently in Richard's direction, motioning him to hurry toward the gate. "Leave!" he shouted.

Clutching his handbag, the one and only possession he carried with him, he made himself walk in the direction he was pointed. Then he was running, stocking-footed, through the open gateway and across the border toward safety.

That was May 2, 1994. Exactly one month had passed since the happy April day when he had driven home for Easter vacation.

35

Come Unto Me

Richard groaned. Something was binding his arm, making it heavy, holding it down. His eyes fluttered, opened, but when he tried to turn his head, everything wavered into an out-of-focus haze. "Wha . . ."

He felt a touch on his other arm. "Richard?" Someone, somewhere was saying his name. "Do you hear me?"

"Uh . . ." He tried to say he could hear, but the words wouldn't come. He wanted to say that he didn't know who was talking, that he didn't know where he was or why.

"It's me. Leon."

Leon? His mind tried to make sense out of the name. Leon was at school. Leon played football. No. That was a long time ago. Before . . . A warm, inviting darkness closed around him again, and he let himself be gathered back into it.

"Richard?" Again that distant voice. And then—he did not know how much later—he was jolted awake. "IV's finished." Someone did something to the heavy arm. "Thank God! The fever's dropping."

"Will he be . . ."

He recognized Leon's voice now and spoke his name.

KILL THY NEIGHBOR

"Richard! You're awake? Praise the Lord!"

"Where am I?"

He heard something about malaria and typhoid fever and bronchitis, but not until days later did Leon let him understand how very sick he had been—telling him about his dangerously high fever, his hallucinations, his feverish talking to his mother, to his father, to Aline—and how a church group had come and prayed that he would be healed. But all Richard could remember was the terrible headache, the nausea, and then nothing except that he had been carried somewhere.

"To this clinic," Leon said.

"Very fortunate," the doctor was saying. "A miracle. If it weren't for your friend here . . ."

A miracle?

In the past months, many things had happened. He remembered the dreadful empty fatigue that first night after he crossed the border. Darkness had fallen by the time he had trudged into the Zairian town of Goma. He was about to pass a hotel when he saw the guard lounging on the porch. "Could I spend the night with you?" he had asked.

The guard motioned toward the hotel door.

Richard shook his head. "No," he said. "With you. Outside." And he reached into his pocket and took out his last bank notes. In return, the guard gave him a tattered piece of cardboard, and Richard huddled on it in the lee of the wall. In the morning, the man was able to direct him to the home of the parents of a former school friend.

"My money's gone." He stood at their door, not knowing what else to say. His money had always taken care of him. At school, he had never had to beg like the peasant children did to have a decent pair of shoes or a shirt or even to pay his tuition. His father had always had enough. Even back when he had needed another school, his father had been able to buy that for him too. And after the killings had started, he had used his and his family's savings to convince friends and soldiers to help. "My money's all gone," he repeated, and he looked into the face of his friend's mother, feeling like a common beggar. She invited him in, and he could see that life had become a daily struggle for her to eke out enough to feed her own family. Yet she kept him and fed him and, knowing how he had suffered, gave him a pair of old thongs to replace his stolen shoes.

That gesture touched him, but he knew he couldn't stay. *I can't. They can't keep me like this forever.* He hunched on their back stoop overlooking Lake Kivu, chin braced on one fist, and stared into the faded blue distance. *But who will help me? Who? When I have no money?*

Money? The question seemed to drop into his mind from nowhere, bringing with it scenes vivid with horror. "I have money." He remembered a voice, calling out again and again that terrible night at the university, pleading, begging, bargaining for his life. "I'll pay!" Richard clenched his eyes tight, trying to blot away how those innocent pleas had been stopped, how they were gruesomely hacked into silence, and how afterward the money had been ripped from the pockets.

"Money." His own voice, now flat and tomblike, repeated the word. "It didn't help others." Knees drawn up, toes pushed under the straps of the old thongs, he made an indelible, though years older, version of the discouraged teenager who feared he would never be able to return to school. *Money didn't help others. Then why me? Why?* Mentally, he flung the question toward the sky, toward the indefinable supreme power whom he had called out to in the attic. *Why?* he demanded. *Why am I here?*

But answers did not come.

In town, he met two former schoolmates, Hutu moderates who had also fled. "Let's go south," they urged him. When they reached Bukavu, a medical aid group hired him temporarily, gave him a white hospital coat, and put him to work treating simple cases among the other refugees. "Doctor, someone's looking for you." The person bringing the message named a meeting place in the camp. He went.

"Richard!"

A shrill voice screamed his name, and his unbelieving eyes recognized the young woman running toward him.

"Marie-Pierre!" he shouted back, and then his voice seized, and they locked themselves in each other's arms. At last, he recovered and held her back and looked at her. She was still the same Marie-Pierre, his little sister, but her face no longer reflected the happy-go-lucky impulsiveness that set her apart from the rest of the family. Instead, she regarded him with the somber gaze of someone who had seen too much that could never be forgotten. "Where are you staying?" he asked.

"The camp."

"Then come with me," he said. He found her a room with a good family who would care for her in a way that would fulfill his promise to their mother. Then on the day when he was to leave again, she clung to him. "Don't go," she begged. "Don't leave me alone."

Gently he made her understand that something inside was pushing him to leave.

"Where?" she asked.

"Maybe South Africa. I'll write," he promised. "And I'll send for you as soon as I'm settled."

"Exposure," the doctor was saying now, telling him the results of the tests they had run at the clinic. "Resistance lowered from sleeping on bare ground so long, in the rain, with no blankets."

That was true. After he left the camp, he and his two friends had traveled at the mercy of the elements on crowded, open-decked boats; atop diesel barrels on overloaded trucks; on borrowed bicycles, riding two or even three to a bike over twisting mountain roads; and on foot, trudging through hostile tropical forests day after long and tiring day. The money he had saved from his work at the camp rapidly disappeared. Finally, all he had was the clothes he wore, an old towel, and the handbag with his documents. The other two had also exhausted their resources, and still they continued, sleeping where they could—usually on the bare ground in the open—and eating what they could find, sometimes going days between meals. Despite that, while they were on the road, they had kept in remarkably good health. It wasn't till he had a roof over his head and a bed of his own and a friend who could care for him that he had become so violently ill.

"Typhoid fever. Malaria. Bronchitis. All at the same time." A person did not have to be a medical student to realize the seriousness of his condition. But he was getting better, he could tell. The doctor said that given a little time, he was going to be fine. Lying in the hospital bed, he began to consider all that had happened, how he had been protected. *Miracles?*

The words of the pastor came back to him, the one who had been on that boat with them. He remembered leaning against the rail as they chugged upriver, listening to the monotonous pulse of the engine and wondering what lay ahead, when the engine had sputtered. Then stopped. Everyone on board groaned—breakdowns happened too frequently. The crew dropped anchor. Richard started toward the shade of the wheelhouse but saw the captain motioning him and his to friends to come. "Why has the engine stopped?" he asked.

The boys looked at one another.

"What did you do to cause the engine to stop?"

To Richard, it sounded like the captain was blaming them. "Well—uh—nothing," he finally said.

"We'll see."

"We didn't do anything!"

"Our boat is for our own people," the captain continued, as though he hadn't heard. "The spirits don't like us to carry foreigners."

So that's it! "Be careful," other passengers had warned. "The spirits are so powerful along here that the captain has a divine as part of his crew on his other boat."

"But we didn't do anything to the engine," Richard insisted.

"We'll see," the captain said again. "My other boat is coming."

When it arrived, he took them aboard it and led them to a door beside the pilothouse. Their footsteps echoed hollowly as they climbed down a narrow set of stairs and turned into a small, dark room. A dull red light glowed on one side, and they could vaguely see the form of another man. He spoke. "The engine of the other boat has stopped," he said.

Yes, we've noticed, Richard would have liked to say, but this was not a time for fun. He tried to make out the man's features, but there was not enough light.

"Now, we are going to find out why. First, I'm going to ask you some questions. If you don't answer truthfully, we'll know. And there will be consequences."

KILL THY NEIGHBOR

Richard felt his heart thudding in his chest. *Consequences.* The other passengers had talked about the bizarre things the river people did.

"Are you foreigners from Rwanda?" he asked.

"Yes," they all answered.

His next questions were directed to them one by one. "Do you have the clothes of a dead person?" he asked.

They think we're murderers! Just because we come from Rwanda. Richard felt almost as if the dark walls were pressing in through the stuffy heat. "No!" he echoed emphatically after the other two.

"Do you have anything belonging to a dead person?"

"No! No!" and "No!" The heat and the dull, eerie light seemed to swallow their answers into meaninglessness.

"We'll see if you are speaking the truth." The form bent down, and Richard felt his breath catch in his chest. A long, thick thing slithered out of the shadows, into the pale path cast by the red light, and it angled across the floor and toward their feet.

Snake! Shivers chased along his spine, but he did not move. He dared not.

"If you are guilty," the words thudded in his ears, "the snake will bite. If the snake bites one of you, that one will be thrown into the river."

The snake continued to creep toward them. Then it turned and began to weave around their feet. *A viper!* Even simple grass snakes made him nervous, but this heavy body sliding past his toes was venomous. Very venomous.

"If the snake doesn't bite," the voice droned, "you have nothing to worry about."

The viper twisted between them, around their feet, back and forth. Richard did not dare even breathe. Stone rigid, feet moored directly in line with the viper's new path, he sensed it drawing back its head as if preparing to strike. And then . . . It turned. And curled away. And returned toward the direction from which it had come.

"That's all for now." The voice did not change tone, did not register approval or disapproval. "You will return to the other boat."

The captain led them back out into the daylight. "If the engine stops again . . ." His voice carried a warning. "We'll know the cause. You will be thrown into the river. Do you understand?"

They all silently nodded.

Somehow the mechanic started the engine, and they continued on their way. *Please.* Richard looked at the wide river and then at the dense forests crowding down into the water on both sides. *Keep the boat running.*

All went well until toward evening the next day. Suddenly, the boat lurched to a stop. "Aground again!" Fear clutched Richard, and he looked around for his friends. Already people were splashing overboard. "Only a couple of kilometers to town," a kindly voice said as someone grabbed his arm. "The river's shallow right across. Come." Without hesitation, he, too, jumped and felt the current catch around his knees as he pushed in the direction of shore.

"You passed the captain's test!" his new friend remarked when they were safely on the path toward the town. "Weren't you afraid?"

"Yes, but we hadn't done anything wrong."

"God has a plan for you," the older man said quietly. "I'm a pastor, and I would like to pray with you before you go on your way."

The three boys continued to travel from place to place. Then Richard found work, temporary to be sure, but enough so he could pause awhile in his wanderings and rent a room and buy food. The others went on. Then came the warning.

"They say you're a spy."

A spy! After his visitor had gone, Richard flung himself onto his bed. *That's why!* For several days, he had sensed that other refugees were drawing back from him, that they didn't really want to be seen with him. *Oh, God!* Since his experience in the attic, he had been praying every morning, asking for protection, for guidance, for blessings on those who had helped him escape, for those who had taken him in during his journeys. There had been so many individuals who had helped that . . . Well, he had almost started to believe that the divine Power was with him, protecting him. But now. *A spy!* His soundless repetition of the charge flung toward the ceiling.

KILL THY NEIGHBOR

The week dragged in prolonged slowness toward its end while Richard dragged himself through the routine that each day demanded. The fellows who had earlier been dropping by to visit did not return. None of those he greeted on the street seemed interested in stopping to talk with him. *Oh, God!* On top of everything else, this new and terrible loneliness was one burden too many, and soundless pleas wrenched from his heart. *Oh, God!* But he did not know to whom he was praying—the God of the Bible or his grandfather's god. They were one and the same, the supreme, all-powerful Imana, and yet . . . *God, please help. Please send me someone.* His thoughts struggled through the night, mixing his prayers with horrible nightmares. When dawn finally came, he forced himself from his bed and into the day. He shuffled down the street, mouthing civil responses to those who greeted him only because politeness had been drilled into him.

"Richard!"

He did not recognize the voice of the one calling his name.

"Richard!"

He stopped and turned. And as if out of a distant haze, he saw a strange but vaguely familiar form.

"It's me! Leon!" His old teammate had hurried across to him. And now in the clinic, Richard saw the Bible lying by the bed, and he knew it was Leon who had brought it and put it there for him, and his eyes traced the gold letters on the book's maroon binding. He was tired, dreadfully tired, and weak, but he knew that God had heard. He had sent Leon. And now Leon was there to care for him as though he were a family brother.

After Richard was discharged from the clinic, the two spent their free time together. "I never got to the university at Mudende as I had hoped." Leon sprawled in a weathered cane chair, its rounded wicker back braced against the trunk of the tree across from Richard's room. "I needed to work first. This year I was ready to go, but . . ." He had already told how Hutu friends had hidden him and smuggled him out of the country. And now . . ." He was the only one in his family to escape; the family holdings had been looted and burned. "How can I go back? There's no one. Nothing."

Richard had been relaxing, with the elbow of his new denim jacket dug into the crooked arm of his other cane chair, his head propped against his knuckles. "I know how you feel."

"Do you think we can ever go back?"

"I don't know." Richard stared toward the clouds drifting above the mango trees lining some distant street. I . . ." He wasn't in the habit of expressing himself to anyone anymore, but with Leon it was different. Leon had told him how he had found God. He would understand. "I've been reading my Bible." He looked down and with the toe of his new shoes traced a crooked cross in the dust. "Jesus forgave the ones who were killing him. Because they didn't understand what they were doing. Like the mobs. The ones who killed my father, my mother, Aline. They didn't know . . ." The familiar something again blocked his throat, and he tensed his neck muscles and forced himself to swallow. "If we can learn to forgive . . ." He broke off again, then said, "Someone gave me a Bible, invited me to Bible studies. The two friends I traveled with, they went to church, and when they came back, they discussed what they had heard. I didn't say anything, but I listened. And now you. Your faith in God. The Christian God. Your prayers. Your friends' prayers. It's as if . . ." Again his voice trailed away.

In the background, music blared from some neighbor's radio, a woman's voice raised as she called out to a friend, a dog was barking, and dust whined up from the tires of a car driving slowly along the street on the other side of the courtyard wall. "My grandmother, my mother, even my father said that Imana had a plan for my life," he finally continued, "but when that pastor from the boat said that God has a plan for me, I knew he meant something different." The gaunt hollowness had disappeared from his face, and since leaving the clinic he had begun to flesh out again. "It's like—through everything that's happened—God's been trying to tell me something. That He's the one who protected me. Not my money. Not anything else. That He . . . oh . . ." Richard's breathy aspiration interrupted what he had started to say, and he turned steady, serious eyes toward Leon. "I see now that He's been trying to let me know He cares for me, and I've decided that this weekend I'm going to start going to church. He has given me life. For now, I don't have any other way to say 'thank you'—to Him, to everyone who's helped me, to you."

"Sha, Richard, my friend." Leon was smiling, but his voice had faded into a husky whisper. "My brother. Stay with God."

On a beautiful Sabbath not many weeks later, Richard was baptized.